D0522044

The Age of
ELECTRONICS

1975 TO 1985

Reader's Digest

Published by The Reader's Digest Association, Inc.
London • New York • Sydney • Montreal

Contents

Introduction   4

THE STORY OF INVENTIONS   18
The personal stereo   20
The autofocus camera   22
Coronary angioplasty   24
The Argos system   25
Test-tube babies   26
Character and speech
recognition   28
Electronic key fobs   30
Trivial Pursuit   30
Rollerblades   31
Black holes   32
STEPHEN HAWKING   36
Compact discs   38
Cyclops   42
Renal ultrasound   42
Minitel   43
Post-it® notes   44
Solar-powered aircraft   45
NEW MATERIALS   46
Portable computers   52
BILL GATES AND STEVE JOBS   56
Wind farms   60
THE ELECTRONICS AGE   62
The TGV   66
COMPUTER PRINTERS   72
The space shuttle   74
THE ARTISTIC SPIRIT OF INVENTION   80

Scanning tunnelling
microscope   86
Airbags   88
Transdermal patches   88
Oncogenics   89
The camcorder   90
KARL VON FRISCH   94
Fractals   96
COMBAT AIRCRAFT   98
Stealth aircraft   102
3-D television   104
The Swatch®   104
The turbosail   105
Mobile phones   106
Genesis of the mobile phone   110
Artificial skin   112
THE QUEST FOR SPEED   113
Genetically modified
organisms   118
THE ECOLOGICAL MOVEMENT   124
The hole in the ozone layer   129
MEDICAL IMAGING   130
PET scans   135
The AIDS virus   136
BOOM TIME IN TOKYO   140

CHRONOLOGY   144
Index   154
Acknowledgments   159

Introduction

The oil crisis of 1973 hit the world economy hard, sparking off a phase of rapid inflation, dwindling manufacturing and widespread structural unemployment. In Western Europe and the United States a period of depression set in, while Eastern Bloc production also ran out of steam. Given the heavy global reliance on oil, problems in the Middle East were always going to spell trouble for the world's economic health. After the Yom Kippur War of 1973, oil-producing Arab nations punished the West for its support for Israel. The situation worsened with the civil war in Lebanon (from 1975), Iran's Islamic Revolution and the Soviet invasion of Afghanistan (1979) and the Iran–Iraq War (1980–8). The pessimistic mood made itself felt in Britain in the punk movement, which famously proclaimed that there was 'no future'. But some signs of optimism shone through in the gloomy mid-1970s world. Long-standing right-wing dictatorships in Greece, Portugal and Spain came to an end, replaced by nascent democracies that in time were embraced by the European Community.

As the 1980s dawned, new governments that were economically liberal but socially conservative came to power in the USA and Britain. For the next decade Ronald Reagan and Margaret

Thatcher presided over a steep decline in manufacturing in favour of new service industries and a deregulated money market. Britain's publicly owned utilities were privatised in a bid to create a 'shareholder democracy'. This was the age of the 'yuppie' (young upwardly mobile professional), when individualism was paramount and, according to Mrs Thatcher, there was 'no such thing as society'. At the same time, faced with the USSR's ruinous attempt to match America in the arms race, Mikhail Gorbachev began reforming the Soviet Union through his policies of *glasnost* and *perestroika*.

With the rise of environmentalism people became more aware of global issues yet also, prompted by the boom in electronic media, they began to withdraw into their individual worlds. This created a dichotomy that is still with us: almost everyone agrees on the need to use less energy and take better care of the planet and its resources, but people are unwilling to relinquish the technology and consumer choice that fuels consumption and growth.

The editors

Sunrise over Tokyo
The Shinjuku business district of Tokyo has one of the most spectacular backdrops in the world – the symmetrical, snow-capped peak of Mount Fuji. Shinjuku also has the busiest railway station in the world, handling more than 2 million passengers every working day.

▶ The first autofocus camera appeared in 1977, but it was the autofocus Nikon F3AF of 1983 that became the camera of choice for press photographers

▼ Housing an audio cassette and a miniaturised set of tape-reading heads attached to a set of stereo headphones, the Walkman® was a neat little device that allowed people to listen to music anywhere, anytime

◀ Introduced in 1978, the Argos global positioning network used 20,000 beacons like this one to track and protect not only ships and aircraft, but also people in peril in remote places and even endangered animal species

As heavy industry and car manufacturing experienced a decline in the wake of the Middle East oil crisis, a new sector of industry was on the rise – electronics. Ever more compact and portable consumer gadgets, such as the Walkman® and the

▼ In the 1980s the American inventor Ray Kurzweil followed up on his optical character recognition system (developed in the late 1970s) with a pioneering speech recognition programme – the image below shows a soundwave pattern from a speech recognition device

tmp.wav   1..200   AUTO

▲ The first test-tube baby, Louise Joy Brown, was born in Oldham, Lancashire on 25 July, 1978, following the successful development of *in vitro* fertilisation by Patrick Steptoe and Robert Edwards

▶ In-line skates were developed by the American ice-hockey-playing Olson brothers in their garage in 1979; their Rollerblade® brand was launched in 1983

camcorder, became an integral part of many people's lives, while the compact disc gave the music industry a shot in the arm. The development of the personal computer and mobile telephone put in place two vital components of the communications revolution that

► In an article published on 1 May, 1978, physicists Peter Young and Wallace Sargent presented convincing evidence for the existence of black holes in the cosmos; this image shows two black holes in the NGC 6240 galaxy

▼ In 1979 Philips and Sony, joint creators of the compact disc, predicted – wrongly, as it turned out – that 'the 1980s will see the end of the vinyl disc and the audio cassette'

▲ A terminal for the Minitel text information service, rolled out across the telephone network in France from 1983 onwards

was just around the corner. The cradle of most of the innovations in electronics was Japan, as forward-looking companies such as Sony, Olympus and Nikon invested heavily in research and product development, perfecting the goods that would bring them success.

▲ The Post-it® note, invented by Art Fry and patented by the 3M company in 1981, proved itself so useful it has since become a ubiquitous piece of office stationery

▲ The first exclusively solar-powered aircraft, the *Solar Challenger*, made its maiden flight from northern France across the Channel in 1981

► The 1980s saw the introduction of a range of new and composite materials designed to offer enhanced performance, such as Gore-Tex®, a fabric that manages to be waterproof on the outside while allowing moisture, such as sweat, to escape from the inside

Elsewhere in industry, the tunnel-effect microscope, which worked at the atomic level, opened the way for the creation of new versatile materials. These would find their way into clothes, cars and homes as a variety of uses were found for the flameproof,

▲ The Osborne 1 and the GriD Compass 1101 (above) were early portable computers, from 1981 and 1982 respectively, but it was 1985 before the first true portables equipped with rechargeable batteries became available

▲ Electronics are everywhere in the modern world, from integrated circuits in digital alarm clocks to the screens in air-traffic control centres (above)

◄ Since 1981, when the first wind farms were constructed in California, wind turbine technology has progressed in leaps and bounds and huge installations are being developed worldwide, like this offshore wind farm at Thorntonbank off the Belgian coast, which came on stream in 2009

anti-bacterial, self-cleaning, non-stick, photovoltaic and other beneficial properties that they offered. Medicine benefited hugely from electronics and computing, which made possible advances such as CT and MRI scanners, scintigraphy and endoscopy.

▲ The US space shuttle programme took off on 12 April, 1981, with the successful maiden flight of *Columbia* from the Kennedy Space Center

▲ The first line of France's TGV network – between Paris and Lyons – came into operation on 22 September, 1981, and while the noise and visual impact of high-speed trains have upset many people, the economic benefits have been considerable

◄ Printer technology saw huge improvements in the 1970s and printer sales rocketed in the 1980s with inkjet and laser devices for the home

With these tools, doctors gained new insight into internal organs. In another key development, it became possible to fertilise a human egg *in vitro*, creating a human embryo that was then implanted into the mother's womb to continue developing as a

▶ In 1982 two researchers at IBM, Gerd Binnig and Heinrich Röhrer, developed the scanning tunnelling microscope, which enabled scientists to move and manipulate atoms, ultimately leading to the creation of nanomaterials

▲ Mathematician Benoît Mandelbrot published *The Fractal Geometry of Nature* in 1982, showing how every small element of a fractal object – such as a snowflake or Romanesco cauliflower (above) – mirrors the structure of the whole, according to the principle of autosimilarity

▲ The optical-illusion known as the Penrose Triangle, a sculpture by the French magician Francis Tabary, is just one of many playful 'non-inventions' devised by artists and scientists to question the nature of perception

normal baby: the birth of the first so-called 'test-tube' baby marked the beginning of assisted reproduction to overcome certain kinds of infertility. In the battle against cancer, the discovery of cancer-causing oncogenes was a major step forward, while rival teams in

◀ Bees have their own 'language', a fact discovered by Austrian zoologist Karl von Frisch; modern studies into the behaviour of bees identify individuals by infrared microchip markers instead of splodges of paint

▲ In 1982, using cells cultivated *in vitro*, researchers isolated a gene associated with causing cancers, leading to the identification of oncogenes; the image above shows an RNA abnormality in a chicken embryo

◀ The Japanese electronics firms Sony and JVC jointly launched the camcorder in 1982, combining a video camera and video recorder

France and the USA managed to identify the cause of AIDS, a terrifying new killer. Other ground-breakers pursued the insatiable human quest for speed: in its ultimate expression, people began to dream of journeying into space with the same ease as they now

▼ The era of 3-D films began when the Human Interface Technology (HIT) Lab at the University of Washington developed a virtual retinal display system that gave the impression of a 3-D image floating in space a metre in front of the viewer

▼ In the 1980s stealth rather than speed became the holy grail of military aircraft designers: the American B-2 Spirit bomber (below) was one of the curious aircraft to emerge from this top-secret development programme

▲ The Cousteau Society's experimental yacht *L'Alcyone* was built in 1985 with turbosails, an environmentally friendly propulsion system that uses the Magnus Effect, first discovered in the 19th century

flew between continents on Earth. The space shuttle was the first step on the road to turning that dream into reality. Combat aircraft advanced hugely in this period – almost beyond recognition in the case of radar-invisible 'stealth' designs. On the ground, Japanese

◀ In 1984 an American medical team pioneered a new technique of using artificially grown skin for grafts on burns victims; the technique later proved useful for treating a wide range of skin conditions

▲ In 1973 the first prototype mobile phone was unveiled in the US and the Federal Communications Commission gave a green llight to the development of a nationwide mobile network; a decade later both the phone and network were a reality, but it would be another decade before phones were as small as this Nokia from 1992

◀ The 20th century was characterised by the human pursuit of speed, personified here by Jamaican runner Usain Bolt, who in 2009 became the fastest sprinter the world had ever seen

and French engineers took rail transport into a new dimension with high-speed trains. But the dark side of all this progress was the growing degradation of the natural environment by human activity. The 1970s and 80s saw a succession of ecological disasters, from

▼ A Belgian company produced the first genetically modified organism (GMO) in 1984, but the development of GMOs since then has been highly controversial

▼ In the 1980s it was proven that the protective ozone layer over Antarctica had been thinning at the rate of 3 per cent a year since at least 1975, leading to the appearance of a large hole at certain times of year

▲ Images like this seabird covered in oil from a tanker spill at sea became almost common-place from the 1980s onwards, symbolising the harmful impact of human activity on the environment

► Set against the spiritual symbolism of Mount Fuji, the business district of Shinjuku in Tokyo epitomised Japan's booming economy in the 1980s

oil spills to nuclear accidents, and the Green movement arose to challenge the pursuit of economic growth at all costs. Although the movement has led to greater awareness of ecological issues and the development of some clean, alternative sources of energy such

◄ Medical imaging, which began with the discovery of X-rays in the late 19th century, came on in leaps and bounds from the 1970s onwards, with the perfecting of MRI scans and scintigraphy (diagnostic nuclear medicine); this image shows a coloured composite 3-D MRI scan of a human brain

▼ The cause of AIDS was identified in 1985, but not before the virus had launched an immunodeficiency pandemic which, despite the efforts of health agencies, continues to ravage many parts of the world – in particular sub-Saharan Africa

as wind farms, the problems of human pollution are still growing. Biotechnology and genetically modified organisms (GMOs) also first emerged in this era, stimulating a fierce debate about their benefits and potential dangers that still rages today.

THE STORY OF INVENTIONS

Within the space of a decade, a multitude of small, portable pieces of technology designed for the individual claimed their place alongside more bulky electronic appliances designed for the home. Personal stereos were soon considered equally 'must-have' possessions as hi-fi systems and TVs. Portable computers and mobile phones – ancestors of today's ubiquitous devices – made their first appearance, starting a process that would see keypads and electronic wizardry create a virtual world, supplanting much of our face-to-face communication.

THE PERSONAL STEREO – 1977
Music on the move

In 1977 a German-Brazilian inventor named Andreas Pavel filed a series of patents for his 'stereobelt', a portable stereo music device. Two years later, the Japanese electronics company Sony launched the Walkman®, a brand that soon became synonymous with personal music players.

Pavel had first tested his device back in 1972, but although he approached several major electronics companies, including Grundig, Yahama and Philips, he failed to ignite their interest. So the first personal portable music player to be manufactured and sold in large numbers was not his stereobelt, it was the Sony Walkman TPS–L2. It operated with audio cassettes, which had been invented by the Dutch electronics firm Philips in 1961. Realising that sales of cassettes would be boosted hugely by the advent of the Walkman, Philips had granted Sony the right to use its product for free.

The Walkman ushered in a whole new way of listening to music: at just 390 grams the compact machine was extremely light for its day and could be taken anywhere, while the headphones made listening a private affair. The only inconvenience was the limited playing time available from the batteries, but this did not stop the Walkman TPS–L2 gaining a loyal following from the moment it appeared in the shops on 1 July, 1979. Sales soared from 1980 onwards, as consumers embraced the idea of a personal stereo system. All of a sudden people were using them in the streets, on public transport, in gyms, in waiting rooms – even in classrooms, much to the annoyance of teachers. This little machine captured the public imagination, appealing to all ages and across the social spectrum.

A household name

By 1981, sales of the Sony Walkman had hit 2.5 million; ten years later the figure had risen to 50 million, even though the Walkman was by then facing competition, mainly from other Japanese manufacturers: Toshiba launched the 'Walky' and Aiwa the 'Cassette Boy'. But Sony's market dominance was such that it was their trademarked brand that people wanted and the

First of millions
Sony's first Walkman, the TPS–L2, appeared in 1979; the orange button allowed users to pause the music momentarily to hear what was going on around them. A decade later Sony launched the first model with an auto reverse function.

Trend-setting CEO
The Sony Corporation and its head Akio Morita played a cutting-edge role in the electronic media industry comparable to that of Microsoft and Bill Gates in the world of computer software. Morita, who co-founded the company in 1946 with Masaru Ibuka, is seen here in 1982.

Listen in anywhere
Julia Roberts with a Walkman in the hugely successful romantic comedy Pretty Woman, *released in 1990. Nowadays, waterproof headphones allow people to listen underwater.*

name began to be used as the generic term for all such devices. To date, Sony have sold more than 220 million devices worldwide and the brand is still going strong in the 21st century.

Not everything has been plain sailing. In 1984 Sony's attempt to move into the digital age with the Discman CD player was a failure. The Discman was based on the MiniDisc system, which never caught on. The laser used in this and similar devices to read the discs was a miniaturised version of those installed in larger CD players, combined with an anti-shock mechanism to prevent the sensitive laser from jumping when the player was moved.

By the mid-1990s, cassette players had been largely superseded by digital devices playing full-sized CDs or DAT (Digital Audio Tape). As the popularity of these devices grew, the price came down. In a further development, devices such as the MP3 player and Apple's iPod® made their debut early in the 21st century. These latest examples of personal music players have an ever-growing capacity to store music digitally without the need for CDs or cassettes and they also enabled users to download music from the Internet.

CREDIT WHERE IT'S DUE

Sony's Akio Morita was long credited with being the originator of the portable music system, but the German-Brazilian Andreas Pavel always claimed he got there first and he eventually won a portion of the fortune that Sony made from the Walkman. Following a long drawn-out legal battle and several court-room encounters, he reached an out-of-court settlement with Sony in 2003 – four years after Morita's death – that was reputed to be worth more than $10 million.

THE VERSATILE CASSETTE

For over 30 years, from the early 1960s onwards, the audio cassette (right) enabled people to record music easily at home, helping to promote the spread of popular music. The music industry saw cassettes as a threat to record sales and ran campaigns claiming that 'Home taping is killing music', but in truth many music-lovers continued to buy records (tape reproduction quality could be poor) and cassettes were often used to record from the radio or to create compilation tapes. Cassettes became widely used in both the home and car and were given a new lease of life by the Walkman in the 1980s. The cassette gave rise to audio books for children and adults and became standard equipment in school language-labs. Mini-cassettes were used in Dictaphone machines and even became a data storage device in some early home computers, such as the Sinclair ZX Spectrum.

Clarity in a click

Before the advent of the autofocus mechanism, photographers had to calibrate the camera's focal length and light settings by hand for each picture. The new invention proved a real boon to amateurs, making spoiled images largely a thing of the past. By reducing the emphasis on technical skill, it helped to democratise the photographer's art.

Quickfire camera
The autofocus system on the Nikon F3AF used two special AF Nikkor lenses, the first of their kind, which had focus drives built into the lenses rather than the camera body. The F3AF became popular with press photographers for its quick focusing.

Photography made simple
Digital autofocus cameras are simple to operate and have encouraged many people, young and old, to take up photography. Digital cameras have an internal memory, but for storing, uploading and printing high-resolution images, users add a detachable memory card. These small devices have massive storage capacity, ranging from 2 gigabytes (for about 600 photos) to 32GBs.

Unless aiming for a deliberately unfocused image for artistic effect, a primary aim of most photographers, amateur or professional, is to capture their subject in sharp focus. Traditional cameras tackled the problem of focusing people or objects at varying distances by means of a telemetric focusing system, which superimposed in the viewfinder two separate images of the subject, seen from different angles. The discrepancy in the apparent position of the object – a phenomenon known as parallax, which also operates in our own binocular vision – enabled the photographer to measure how far away the object was. By turning a focus ring, which moved a system of lenses within the camera by means of a helical screw, the two images in the viewfinder were brought together in order to obtain a sharp image.

Autofocus (AF) works on the same principle, but instead of manual adjustment it relies on a sensor and a small drive motor to adjust the lens and attain optimal focus. As a result of miniaturisation, most modern cameras incorporate an AF system where the motor is built into the camera body or the lens itself is motorised. If desired, AF can be deactivated. On some models, the autofocus adapts itself to the focal length of the lens, allowing the photographer to alter the depth of field by manipulating the camera's aperture setting and shutter speed.

Growing sophistication

Japanese technology led the way. The world's first production AF camera, using traditional 35mm film, was the Konica C35AF in 1977. This 'point-and-shoot' model incorporated an electro-mechanical autofocus system controlled by an integrated circuit. In 1978 the US company Polaroid responded with the SX-70, the first autofocus single-lens reflex (SLR) camera. The Japanese Pentax ME-F, which used focus sensors in the camera body coupled with a motorised lens, was the first autofocus 35mm SLR in 1981.

In the spring of 1983 Nikon launched its revolutionary F3AF, while in 1985, the Minolta Maxxum 7000 pioneered the integrated autofocus system in which the AF sensors and the focusing drive were housed in the camera body. This model, which also had a motor to wind the film on automatically, set the standard for later cameras. Nowadays, autofocus is a standard function found in all cameras, from compacts, through 35mm or digital SLRs, to camcorders and cameras in mobile phones.

Active and passive

Active autofocus, which is commonly installed in compact cameras, 35mm SLRs and analogue camcorders, is ideal for photographing subjects where the contrast is low. It focuses by means of a rangefinding system that transmits and receives infrared light in order to triangulate the distance to the subject. A servomotor then adjusts the lens accordingly. The degree of precision depends on the quality of the components, but active systems tend not to focus well on objects close to the camera.

Passive autofocus is less effective in conditions of low light or low contrast. It works by splitting the beam of incoming light into pairs of images and comparing them. Optical prisms capture the light rays and divert them to an AF sensor. The shutter release on cameras equipped with passive autofocus operates in two phases: light pressure on the button causes the sensors to analyse the scene and achieve optimal focus, while pressing more firmly takes the picture.

Through their autofocus function, which automatically resolves technical questions of shutter speed and aperture setting, compact digital cameras enable even amateurs to take pictures of consistent quality. The phenomenal success of the mobile phone, with its camera function, has seen candid photography become almost a reflex reaction.

RANGEFINDERS

The rangefinder is an optical instrument that measures the distance of an object from the observer through a system of lenses and mirrors that coordinate two separate images. The principle was formulated in 1777 by French astronomer Alexis Marie Rochon, but it was 1922 before the first practical rangefinder was introduced to help ballistics experts work out artillery trajectories. In early examples, the larger the apparatus (on average 4m across), the more accurate the reading. Modern rangefinders are far more compact (in many cases small enough to fit in a digital camera), while purpose-built instruments are used by the armed forces and surveyors.

Lie of the land
Modern geodetic surveying instruments are equipped with active autofocus systems that can measure distances with remarkable accuracy. Here (above), an oil company geologist surveys a prospective oilfield in the Libyan desert to evaluate its susceptibility to earth tremors.

Pin sharp picture
Tower Bridge in London, seen through the viewfinder of a digital camera. Modern compact cameras tend to focus on one area of the image, whereas more sophisticated cameras select multiple focus points.

Life-saving scaffold
This artificially coloured X-ray image shows the mesh of a stent supporting the walls of a patient's coronary artery after undergoing angioplasty. By enlarging the artery, the stent ensures a steady flow of blood to the heart.

Coronary angioplasty 1977

A heart attack – or to give it the proper medical term, myocardial infarction – is caused, among other things, by obstruction of the coronary arteries resulting in the cardiac muscle being starved of oxygenated blood from the lungs. The standard treatment for this condition today is angioplasty, a procedure that dilates a narrowed artery, often teamed with fibrinolysis, a process whereby the fibrous protein that causes the blood to clot is broken down through injection of the enzyme plasmin.

By accident and design

The first coronary angioplasty was performed in Zurich in 1977 by the German surgeon Andreas Gruentzig. This medical breakthrough built on several earlier discoveries. In 1929 the German physician Werner Forssmann inserted a flexible catheter into a vein in his forearm and threaded it through to his heart, recording the feat with an X-ray photograph of the catheter in his right atrium. Forssmann's bold experiment eventually earned him the Nobel prize for medicine in 1956. An Ohio hospital radiologist discovered cardiac angiograms in 1958 when he accidentally injected a large quantity of dye into a patient's coronary arteries: the doctors were able to observe the blood flow into the heart and thus identify the clogged arteries. In 1964 the American radiologist Charles Dotter demonstrated that a blocked femoral (leg) artery could be dilated

STENTS

The technique of angioplasty was improved in 1985 by the introduction of the stent, a small wire-mesh tube attached to the balloon, which fixes to the internal wall of the artery and stops the vessel from closing again. The first stents were made of bare metal, but from 2002 onwards, drug-eluting stents have become increasingly common. These are coated with drugs that slowly release to block excessive cell proliferation (fibrosis) on the artery wall.

by introducing a series of ever larger rigid catheters, but the trauma to the blood vessels prevented the procedure being widely adopted.

In 1974 Andreas Gruentzig had the idea of replacing the rigid dilating catheters with a small inflatable balloon inserted with the help of two catheters, one on top of the other. Opaque fluid was injected through one catheter to highlight the narrowed artery, while the other was used to insert the balloon and then inflate and deflate it within the artery. He tested his technique on a renal (kidney) artery before applying it to coronary arteries. Millions of coronary angioplasties are now performed every year. The double catheter is inserted either through an artery in the arm or in the groin. The same technique works on femoral, renal and carotid (neck) arteries.

Standard procedure
Angioplasties (top left) are straightforward procedures that usually involve local rather than general anaesthetic and take no more than 30 minutes to two hours. The clinical team uses X-ray equipment to monitor the progress of the catheter into the narrowed artery, taking an image every five seconds.

The Argos system 1978

A rgos is a satellite-based environmental data-gathering system. Established in 1978, it is the fruit of international collaboration between NASA, the French space agency CNES and the National Oceanic and Atmospheric Administration (NOAA), among other organisations. Argos utilises the Doppler effect, a physical principle first identified in the 19th century whereby the frequency of a wave changes when the transmitter and receiver are moving relative to one another.

The Argos network comprises six satellites in low polar orbit positioned at an altitude of 850km, each covering a circle 5,000km across. As each satellite passes overhead, transmitters on Earth have a window of 10 minutes in which to send signals to the satellite's receiver.

Worldwide protection

Information picked up from the 20,000 radio beacons or 'platforms' around the globe is relayed by the satellites to 50 ground stations. In turn, these transmit data to two processing centres – in Washington, DC and Toulouse, France – where the position of each beacon can be pinpointed to within 150m. To aid maritime safety, the locations of ships are beamed to all users within 15 minutes of being received.

The numerous applications of Argos range from ocean observation to environmental protection and fisheries management. Small Argos transmitters fitted to animals mean that they can be tracked for conservation purposes. Meanwhile, beacons on buoys provide climate researchers with invaluable data on ocean currents and sea temperature. Argos continues to evolve, with the fourth generation of transmitters due to enter service in 2014.

INTERNATIONAL RESCUE

C ospas-Sarsat, a spin-off from Argos, is a search-and-rescue network set up in 1979 by the USA, the USSR, Canada and France; many other countries have joined the network since. It uses a combination of low-orbiting and geostationary satellites that can pinpoint the location of aircraft, ships or even mountaineers in distress. It has saved thousands of lives since becoming fully operational in 1984.

Global network
The Argos system has various applications and is installed on all kinds of ocean-going vessels and buoys.

Keeping track
Miniature transmitters, like that mounted on the back of the turtle (above), enable biologists to follow the migrations of many different animal, bird and fish species.

The advent of IVF

Louise Brown came into the world on 25 July, 1978. The extraordinary thing about the birth of baby Louise was that fertilisation of the egg by the sperm had taken place outside her mother's body, then the embryo was reimplanted into the womb to continue its normal development. This was the first successful example of human in vitro fertilisation, better known as IVF. It was the culmination of 12 years of work by surgeons Patrick Steptoe and Robert Edwards to overcome sterility.

Lesley and John Brown, from Oldham in Lancashire, had tried and failed to have a baby. Lesley suffered from tubal sterility. The Fallopian tubes, which link the ovaries to the uterus, are where the sperm meets the released egg and fertilisation takes place. The egg then continues its journey to the uterus, where the embryo develops. If the Fallopian tubes become blocked, a woman cannot conceive naturally. In 1976 Lesley was referred to Dr Patrick Steptoe, the resident gynaecologist and obstetrician at Oldham and District General Hospital. At the time, he was working with Cambridge physiologist Dr Robert Edwards on the problem of female sterility.

Fertile collaboration

Like most scientists, Steptoe and Edwards built on the work of predecessors. The first attempts at in vitro fertilisation and reimplantation of the embryo in the womb took place in the late 19th century. In 1935 the American biologist Gregory Pincus pioneered in vitro fertilisation with rabbits, which led to his compatriot Dr Min Chang successfully breeding rabbits using the method in 1959.

Towards the end of the 1960s, stimulation of egg production through the injection of the hormone gonadotropin became widespread in fertility treatment. In 1965, after several years of research, Robert Edwards found the optimum conditions for activating the dormant and immature egg cells in vitro and promoting their maturation. He discovered that human eggs required 24 hours of incubation before the maturation process began.

Patrick Steptoe was an expert in the new technique of laparoscopy, by which the female reproductive tract can be visually examined through an endoscope inserted through a small incision in the abdomen. Embarking on their joint venture, Steptoe first used gonadotropin to stimulate ovulation in their sterile women volunteers, then used laparoscopy techniques to harvest the egg cells (oocytes) from the ovaries. Edwards concentrated on fertilising the oocytes by bringing them into contact with the father's spermatozoa in vitro – literally 'in glass', as in a test tube. The fertilised egg (embryo) was kept in a special solution for four or five days until it had divided into 64 cells before being transferred back into the woman's uterus.

Within a few years, Steptoe and Edwards had mastered the technique of in vitro fertilisation, but their first hundred attempts at implanting embryos failed, ending in short-lived pregnancies that spontaneously aborted. Their efforts were finally rewarded in 1978, yet even then the pregnancy was a touch-and-go affair, and due to Lesley's high blood pressure Louise was delivered by Caesarean section.

Small miracle
The day after the birth of Louise Brown (left), the world's first 'test-tube' baby, the press was bursting with reports on the revolutionary new procedure that had brought her into the world. The second baby to be created by IVF treatment was born later the same year in Calcutta, India. Nowadays, between 50 and 70 per cent of IVF treatments are successful, with each patient undergoing an average of six attempts. Around 25 to 30 per cent result in multiple births.

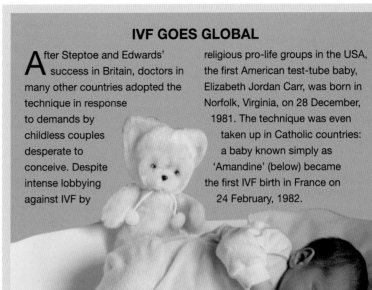

IVF GOES GLOBAL

After Steptoe and Edwards' success in Britain, doctors in many other countries adopted the technique in response to demands by childless couples desperate to conceive. Despite intense lobbying against IVF by religious pro-life groups in the USA, the first American test-tube baby, Elizabeth Jordan Carr, was born in Norfolk, Virginia, on 28 December, 1981. The technique was even taken up in Catholic countries: a baby known simply as 'Amandine' (below) became the first IVF birth in France on 24 February, 1982.

Routine procedure

The birth of Louise Brown gave rise to an impassioned debate about the desirability of IVF. Opponents of assisted reproductive technology falsely claimed that IVF treatment increased the likelihood of birth defects. Beyond this, IVF raised many ethical issues, chief among them the destruction of human embryos that is involved in the procedure. This raised the thorny question of exactly when does life commence – at the point of conception, or after 24 weeks, when the foetus is 'viable' (that is, has some chance of survival if born prematurely)? Can an embryo be considered a person, or is it only a potential person? These questions met with very different responses according to country, religion and culture.

For women desperate to overcome infertility, such arguments were irrelevant. Steptoe and Edwards' work paved the way for medically assisted procreation (MAP), which to date has been instrumental in the birth of more than 3 million children worldwide.

COMBATING MALE STERILITY

While IVF constitutes the main treatment for female sterility, male sterility – usually caused by a low sperm count – has benefited from a procedure known as intracytoplasmic sperm injection (ICSI). The technique, developed in the USA in 1992 by the Italian doctor Gianpiero Palermo, involves a single sperm cell (obtained either from ejaculated sperm or directly from the testicles) being injected into the egg for fertilisation. Other methods of medically assisted procreation (MAP) include intrauterine insemination, implantation of embryos frozen from earlier IVF treatments and the use of either eggs or sperm from third-party donors.

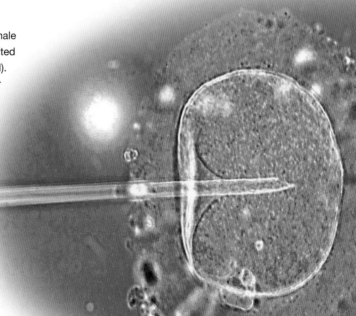

Starting point of life

Intracytoplasmic sperm injection (ICSI, right) is an IVF procedure in which a single spermatozoon from the father is injected into an egg through a micropipette. Fertilised eggs are then implanted in the mother's womb. The success rate for the procedure is around 20 per cent.

Character and speech recognition 1978

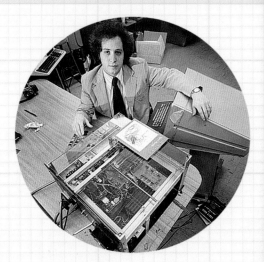

In 1976 Ray Kurzweil, an American computer programmer, developed a print-to-speech reading machine for the blind. Working on much the same lines as a photocopier, a computer digitised the text on a page and read it back aloud. This revolutionary software was a real breakthrough, giving non-sighted people potential access to all printed works, even those that had not been translated into Braille. Comprising a scanner and a voice synthesising unit, the machine was unveiled to the public in 1978. One instant devotee was Stevie Wonder, the blind singer-songwriter, who went into partnership with Kurzweil in 1982 to develop a keyboard that even a blind person could use to re-create the instrumentation of an orchestra.

First steps in speech recognition

Thirty years earlier, in 1952, the Swiss inventor Jean Dreyfus-Graf unveiled the 'phonetograph'. This device was hooked up between a tape recorder and an oscilloscope, and divided the sound wave into phonetic elements. At the same time, optical character recognition (OCR) appeared when cryptanalyst David Shepard was commissioned by the US National Security Agency to write a program for converting messages into computer language. The first commercial OCR document reader was installed by *Reader's Digest* magazine in 1955.

IT prodigy
Ray Kurzweil (right) was gifted in computer science. Aged just 12, he wrote a statistical program that was bought by IBM. He is seen here with his print-to-speech reading machine for the blind, the Kurzweil 1000.

Rapid reader
The world's fastest book scanner is the Digitizing Line (below), used by major libraries. With an automatic page-turning system and the ability to recognise a huge variety of fonts, it can convert print into machine-encoded text at a rate of 3,000 pages an hour.

Problems of calibration

Whether treating speech or text characters, the main problem of these systems, even today, is that they require a great deal of calibration to produce a sufficiently accurate end result. Some words and phrases appear inaccurately rendered when the reconstituted OCR text is proofread against the original. It has proved very difficult to construct computer programs for comparing the scanned letters to a base library of symbols, even when sophisticated syntactical and grammatical dictionaries are brought into play.

The best results are obtained from applications that accurately identify all the diverse forms of letters in a huge variety of different fonts. Even so, ligatures are still a major sticking-point. Such software is expensive and therefore often restricted to official civil service tasks or large book digitisation projects, such as the Project Gutenberg free online e-book resource.

His Master's Voice

In trying to overcome the many difficulties posed by continuous speech, voice recognition systems have benefited from the huge growth in computer power. Recorded through a microphone, speech is initially broken down into individual signals that are compared with a set of basic acoustic paradigms stored within the program. Once the phonemes, or 'sound segments', have been recognised, they are reconstituted into the words that they most closely resemble that are contained in a sound archive dictionary. This is the point at which errors are most likely to occur if insufficient groundwork has been invested in ironing out bugs in the program.

Speech recognition programs have been applied to automate some cockpit functions in military fighter aircraft, so reducing the pilot's

.wav   1..200   AUTO

Acoustic fingerprint?
An artist's impression of the sound wave pattern produced by a speech recognition program (above). The amplitude and frequency of each voice generates a unique wave pattern. Police forces are investigating the identification possibilities of such technology.

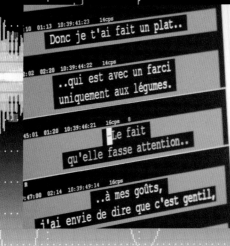

Direct transcription
Voice recognition software allows users to bypass computer interfaces such as the computer and mouse. This is especially useful in situations that would otherwise demand the keying in of large amounts of text – for example, in subtitling TV programmes (above)

workload. The technology as pioneered in French Mirage fighters in 1983. It has since been adopted by the US and Swedish air forces and is installed in the Eurofighter Typhoon. Voice recognition software was developed, from 1988 onwards, to enable home computer users to dictate documents directly without typing: Dragon Dictate and Microsoft Voice Command are two popular applications.

In practice, the use of voice recognition systems is still limited – some automated telephone options are activated by speech, plus some SatNav units respond to voice commands – but penetration of the software

THE KATALAVOX SYSTEM

Katalavox is a speech recognition system developed by the French researcher Martine Kempf in the early 1980s. The name is a hybrid of Greek and Latin meaning literally 'understand voice' and the system was designed to be used in cars specially adapted for the disabled. With Katalavox, the voice activates a variety of functions in the car including lights, indicators, windscreen wipers and the horn. The world's first electric wheelchair directed by Katalavox was unveiled in London in 1983 at the convention of the International Society of Prosthetics and Orthetics.

is set to increase in the future. The development of 'smart houses' opens up possibilities for lighting, security systems and home appliances to be controlled by voice commands.

Electronic key fobs 1978

In 1978 Paul Lipschutz, director of the Neiman-Valeo car parts firm at Croissy-sur-Seine near Paris, invented the electronic key fob, a device now in almost universal use. Pressing it lightly with the thumb sends an infrared signal that locks or unlocks the vehicle from some distance away. The first car to incorporate the technology was the 1982 Renault Fuego hatchback. More advanced fobs can unlock and start the engine without the need for a key. In France, the device is called 'le Plip', which is a contraction of the inventor's name, but many people think the term comes from the small electronic sound emitted by some remote keyless systems.

Trivial Pursuit 1979

On 15 December, 1979, journalists Scott Abbott and Chris Haney were on assignment in Spain with time on their hands when they found that some pieces were missing from their Scrabble set. So instead of playing Scrabble they devised their own board game, a general knowledge-based quiz that they called Trivial Pursuit. Back home in Canada, Haney's brother John and a friend, Ed Werner, helped them to develop the idea. By late 1981 they were ready to trademark the game and in 1982 they released 1,100 copies. Initial sluggish sales were boosted by word-of-mouth recommendations. By 1984 the game had become a craze across North America with 20 million sold. By 2010, global sales in 33 countries had reached 100 million. Now in 19 languages, it is the world's third most popular board game, after Scrabble and Monopoly.

Board-game brainwave
Trivial Pursuit made a fortune for its inventors, Scott Abbott and Chris and John Haney (left). From its original format (above), the game has diversified into many editions, aimed at different age groups or specialising in particular subjects. An online edition was launched in 2003.

Sleek conveyance
This streamlined high-performance skate, incorporating carbon fibre, was launched in 2005 to mark the 25th anniversary of the Rollerblade company.

The new skates found a market ready and waiting among young people, setting off a craze for in-line skating that mushroomed in the 1980s and 90s. Olson's product was so successful that the name became the generic term for all skates of this type. Today, in-line skates have diversified into a wide range of models designed for different activities and with varying wheel sizes for particular skating styles – from artistic in-line skating (the equivalent of figure skating on ice) and roller hockey to freestyle slalom and speed skating. Despite roller hockey being introduced as a demonstration sport at the 1992 Summer Olympiad in Barcelona, rollerblading has not yet managed to propel itself into the arena of full Olympic activities.

Rollerblades 1979

In 1979 Scott and Brennan Olson, two ice-hockey-playing brothers from Minneapolis, USA, discovered an old pair of in-line rollerskates in their parents' garage. They had been made in the 1960s by the Chicago Roller Skate Company and were designed for off-season training by ice-hockey players in summer. Basically, they were ice skates with a set of polyurethane wheels attached, but they inspired Scott Olson to create the Rollerblade. He worked out a way of making the blade length adjustable and also came up with a dual-bearing wheel that ran faster. He then founded his own company to market the new improved skate and patented the design in 1981. The Rollerblade trademark was established in 1983.

Skating challenge
With obvious similarities to skateboarding, the style known as 'aggressive in-line skating' involves spectacular stunts performed on specially built ramps in skate-parks or over street obstacles.

FAST ON THE BEAT

A number of police forces around the world have formed small squads of officers equipped with in-line skates. A French rollerblading unit was formed in Paris in 1998 to help police the Football World Cup staged that year. In Indonesia officers are deployed on skates to patrol traffic-clogged Jakarta, where they can reach incidents far faster than in cars. Similar units operate in Florida, California, Brussels and Amsterdam. There is also a patrol in London's Hyde Park, but there are drawbacks: they cannot skate over grass and they cannot work in the rain, when pavements and streets become too slick for the wheels to grip effectively.

Cosmic monsters in our midst

On 1 May, 1978, American physicists Peter Young and Wallace Sargent advanced strong, if indirect, evidence of a supermassive black hole in galaxy M87. Their seminal paper prompted fellow scientists to go in search of these cosmic monsters, whose existence had up till then been doubted.

Young and Sargent's paper, entitled 'Dynamical evidence for a central mass concentration in the galaxy M87', appeared in the *Astrophysical Journal* and was an important milestone in astrophysics. They put forward a substantial raft of observational evidence to indicate that the M87 galaxy, which is situated in the Virgo cluster some 55 million light years from Earth, contains at its centre a body with a mass of 6.6 billion times that of our Sun. The diameter of the volume of space it occupies is such that it could swallow our solar system. This makes it the largest such phenomenon yet measured.

A consequence of relativity

Einstein's general theory of relativity had predicted that such a concentration of matter must, of necessity, generate what is known

Jet power
Galaxy M87 in an image taken by NASA's Chandra X-ray telescope, built to study high-energy phenomena like black holes and quasars. The jet emerging from the centre is thought to be produced by strong electromagnetic forces created by matter swirling towards a supermassive black hole. These forces pull gas and magnetic fields in a narrow jet away from the black hole along its axis of rotation.

as a 'gravitational singularity' – a kind of microscopic tear in the fabric of the spacetime continuum that would swallow all surrounding matter. Thereafter, short of discounting the growing amount of evidence available from observation – or taking the unthinkable step of denying the relativity theory – physicists had no option but to accept that black holes really did exist. The discovery of the M87 black hole sent shockwaves through the astrophysics world. Researchers directed their telescopes at the heart of similar galaxies, avidly scanning for signs of other such phenomena.

Birth of a stellar black hole
An artist's impression of the flash of gamma rays produced at the formation of a stellar black hole.

PROVING THAT THE BLACK HOLE EXISTS

Peter Young and Wallace Sargent, both researchers at the California Institute of Technology (CalTech), based their analysis of M87 on images obtained through a technology that had only recently been introduced into astronomy – the charge-coupled device (CCD) spectrometer, an instrument highly sensitive to light waves. This enabled them on the one hand to spot radio emissions and powerful jets of matter issuing from the central zone of the galaxy (indicating unusual activity), and on the other hand to conduct a detailed analysis of the light spectrum of the stars around its core. All these observations pointed to a huge concentration of matter moving at unusually high speed around the centre of the galaxy – a strong indication of the presence of a black hole.

The event horizon

The initial scepticism of some scientists is understandable given what an extraordinary thing a black hole is. Technically speaking, it is a star comprising two elements. At its centre is a gravitational singularity, a minute point less than 10^{-43} in diameter yet of practically infinite mass, whose gravitational pull attracts all matter. Around this develops a spherical area of indeterminate volume – from a few kilometres to millions of kilometres across – whose outer limit is called the 'event horizon'.

Event horizons are aptly named: any matter or light (energy) crossing the event horizon boundary is inexorably pulled into the black hole. According to the theory of general relativity, at the event horizon spacetime curves like a bottomless well, trapping every particle. Since even photons share this fate, black holes reflect no light and so cannot be seen directly. They reveal their presence through the effect on the space around them, and by this means astronomers can monitor them.

Three types of black hole

Decades of observation have yielded a list of a million potential black holes of varying dimensions, categorised as supermassive, intermediate-mass or stellar. The largest are the supermassive black holes, like M87, and these are the easiest to track: we know that they are always found at the centre of their host galaxy and they generate a high level of activity, such as X-ray emissions and jets, which makes them observable. Intermediate-mass black holes,

Two into one
The galaxy NGC 6240 (top) was formed by two galaxies merging. Their nuclei – the distinct bright source at the centre – is actually two supermassive black holes 3,000 light years apart. After several hundred million years, they will coalesce into a single, even more massive black hole. Above right: The Chandra observatory, which was placed in orbit by the shuttle Columbia *in 1999.*

comprising between 100 and 10,000 solar masses, are far more tricky to flush out and observational evidence is still contested. Stellar black holes, formed by the death of stars between eight and 100 solar masses, are thought to be numerous, but their small size makes their effects on their immediate environment hard to observe. Behind the different types of black hole is the same basic phenomenon: the gravitational collapse of one or more stars into themselves.

Einstein's misgivings

It was a colleague of Einstein's, the German physicist Karl Schwarzschild, who just a few months after the publication of the General Theory of Relativity in 1916 demonstrated that

---

JOURNEY OF NO RETURN

What would become of a spaceship if it was drawn into a black hole? Assuming that it was not immediately torn to pieces by the extreme gravitational 'tides' that exist at the event horizon, those on board would notice the passage of time accelerating (time dilation). On crossing the event horizon, there would be no way back: the amount of energy required to escape from the black hole would be infinite, so the ship would be inescapably drawn towards the gravitational singularity. By contrast, to anyone observing from Earth the progress of the ship would seem to slow down, coming to a stop when it reached the singularity.

PRIMORDIAL BLACK HOLES

These hypothetical black holes are microscopic, the size of elementary particles. They were formed not by stellar core collapse, but by the extreme density of matter in the early expansion of the universe.

Sagittarius star
A supermassive black hole known as Sagittarius A (inset below) was found at the centre of the Milky Way in 1974. A leading expert on the phenomenon is Professor Andreas Eckart, shown here (below) inspecting the huge Effelsberg radio telescope in Germany.

Einstein's equations necessarily postulated a singularity where the gravitational field became infinite. But, in common with Einstein himself, Schwarzschild regarded this as a purely mathematical hypothesis.

During the 1920s other physicists became interested in the strange singularity hypothesis and demonstrated that a singularity of this kind would form an event horizon. By the end of the decade the hypothesis had become a physical possibility through the work of the Indian astrophysicist Subrahmanyan Chandrasekhar. He showed that a dying star collapses under its own weight, thus decreasing in volume, since its radiation can no longer counterbalance its gravitational force. If the

star's mass exceeds a certain threshold – the so-called Chandrasekhar Limit, which equals 1.44 solar masses – collapse ensues, leading to the formation of a spacetime singularity. All matter that is sufficiently compact will behave in this way; for example, if the Earth were compressed into a volume of no more than a few cubic centimetres, or the Sun into 3 cubic kilometres, this process would be set in train.

Final confirmation

The hypothesis was corroborated in 1939 when the American physicists Robert Oppenheimer and Hartland Snyder suggested that neutron stars – hyperdense stars whose existence had been proposed by the Swiss astronomer Fritz Zwicky five years earlier – might be prime examples of the phenomenon of gravitational collapse. This was the first scientific prediction of black holes. Models of stellar evolution soon indicated that neutron stars were the remnants of massive stars (stars of more than 8 solar masses) after a supernova event. None of these hypotheses could be confirmed through observation, but in 1963 the New Zealand astronomer Roy Kerr suggested that objects coming close to a rotating black hole would be caught up in its motion, due to the curvature of spacetime. Here, at last, was an observable astronomical phenomenon.

The discovery of the first neutron star in 1967 confirmed the theory of black holes. The term itself was coined around this same time by US physicists Kip Thorne and John Wheeler. In 1971 the first potential stellar black hole was identified when the galactic X-ray source Cygnus X-1 was found to be a binary system (two stars orbiting each other). The discovery of M87 in 1978 promoted the hypothesis of black holes into a scientific certainty. Since then, discoveries of black holes have come thick and fast, such as the double supermassive black holes in the galaxy NGC 6240 or the quasi-stellar object Q0906+6930, the most remote black hole yet observed at 12.7 billion light years from Earth. Even the centre of our own galaxy, the Milky Way, has been found to contain a black hole, now named Sagittarius A, containing more than 4 million solar masses of matter.

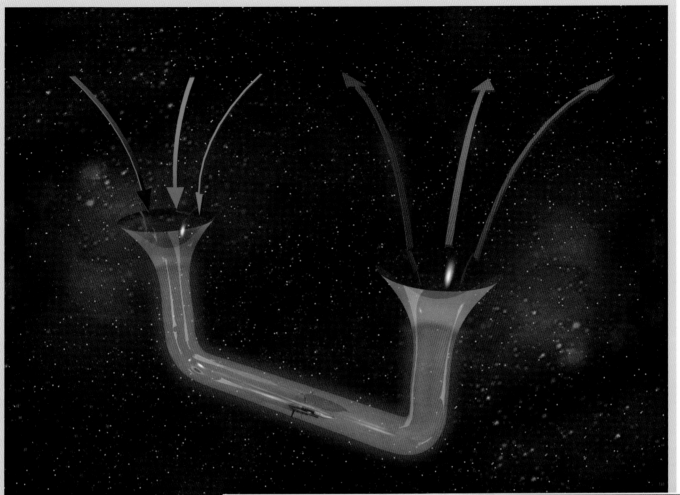

WHITE HOLES AND WORM HOLES

Astrophysicists have postulated that black holes might represent portals to cosmic 'worm holes', a kind of shortcut or bridge in spacetime. At the hypothetical far end of a worm hole would be a 'white hole' – a region of spacetime that cannot be entered but from which matter and energy are expelled. The artist's impression above illustrates the construct, with a tunnel through spacetime connecting a black hole drawing in matter (on the left) and a white hole expelling it (right). No observational evidence has so far been found to confirm the presence of either white holes or worm holes.

Distinguishing science fact from fiction *Supermassive black holes are cosmic monsters that draw in and absorb all matter surrounding them. This artist's impression (above) shows a supermassive black hole surrounded by a doughnut-shaped cloud of black dust. According to the theory of relativity, black holes could curve spacetime to form a connection between two distant points of the universe. But the notion that a spaceship could travel through such a worm hole (top) and emerge intact in a different universe is pure science fiction.*

STEPHEN HAWKING
An indomitable intellect

Stephen Hawking was born in Oxford on 8 January, 1942, three hundred years to the day after the death of Galileo. A highly gifted but somewhat idle student, he eventually opted to study cosmology. While conceding that such theoretical subjects did not help to 'feed anyone or get their wash whiter', he gave an eloquent defence of their ultimate value: 'We all need to understand where we came from and these observations show us a glimpse of our origin.'

As Hawking himself admitted, when he was a student at University College, Oxford – he graduated in 1962 – he spent more time coxing rowing teams than studying his degree subject of natural sciences. But even then his health had begun to decline seriously. Doctors diagnosed him as suffering from amyotrophic lateral sclerosis, a form of motor neurone disease, and rated his chances of surviving far into adulthood as slim. This progressive wasting disease causes people to lose the use of their limbs and become quadriplegic, but in Hawking's case it developed more slowly than anticipated. In 1964 he married Jane Wilde, with whom he had three children; they separated in 1991 and subsequently divorced.

Challenging orthodoxies

Progressing into astronomy, Hawking first came to prominence for his groundbreaking attempts to unify two theories that had hitherto been seen as mutually contradictory: Einstein's General Theory of Relativity concerning the infinitely large and the laws of quantum mechanics which pertain to the infinitely small. By transposing the formulae written by his friend and colleague, the mathematician Roger Penrose, Hawking's first major breakthrough was to demonstrate that the instant of the Big Bang itself – the very beginning of spacetime – represented a gravitational singularity. Since all matter and energy were contained within an infinitely small volume, it was a black hole whose density and pressure were infinite.

Following in Newton's footsteps, Hawking became Lucasian Professor of Mathematics at Cambridge in 1979 and continued his research into black holes and quantum mechanics. One of his key findings was that that they were not as black as previously assumed, as they emit some thermal radiation. The discovery of 'Hawking radiation' sealed his international academic reputation. The complex calculations that his work entailed were all the more remarkable in that he performed most of them in his head, having lost the use of his hands. In 1997 he stated that all information swallowed by a black hole is irretrievably lost. But seven years later, when his own work conclusively proved this not to be the case, he did not hesitate to publicly acknowledge his error.

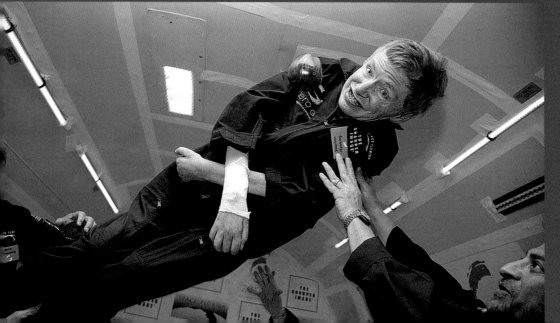

Space advocate
Stephen Hawking firmly believes that the future of the human race lies in space. On 26 April 2007 he joined a NASA zero-gravity practice mission, where trainee astronauts briefly experience weightlessness in an aircraft in a parabolic flight path. This was in preparation for becoming one of the first passengers on commercial sub-orbital spaceflights.

Inexorable pull

All matter and energy, in the form of light, in the vicinity of a black hole is pulled in by the curvature of spacetime.

Interpreter of our origins

Stephen Hawking (left) on 15 September, 2009, at a conference to mark the 450th anniversary of the founding of the University of Geneva.

A great populariser

As well as being a brilliant and eminent physicist, Hawking emerged as a gifted exponent of popular science. *A Brief History of Time*, his first book explaining quantum physics and the Big-Bang Theory to the general public, was published in 1988 and became a bestseller. Since then he has published *The Universe in a Nutshell* (2001) and, with his daughter Lucy, *George's Secret Key to the Universe* (2007). Defying the prognosis of his condition and despite the tightening grip of disability, Hawking continues to conduct research and promote the cause of science from his motorised wheelchair with the aid of a voice synthesiser. As he puts it himself: 'It's a waste of time to be angry about my disability. One has to get on with life and I haven't done badly. People won't have time for you if you are always angry or complaining.'

EXPLAINING THE BIG QUESTIONS

In 1988, in his first book of popular science, *A Brief History of Time: From the Big Bang to Black Holes*, Stephen Hawking set out to answer such profound cosmological questions as 'Where does the universe come from?', 'How and why did it begin?' and 'Will it come to an end, and if so, how?' His aim in writing the book was to provide answers in a way that he hoped would be 'accessible to a person with no scientific background'. He therefore banished all mathematical formulae from the text. As he stated in the preface: 'Someone told me that each equation I included in the book would halve the sales.' Instead, he offered clear descriptive explanations of all aspects of current scientific knowledge about the universe, from the Big Bang to black holes, as well as of such famous scientific theories as 'time's arrow' and 'Heisenberg's uncertainty principle'. Though Hawking initially had trouble finding a publisher, the book has since enjoyed phenomenal success, selling over 10 million copies since its release. In 2005 Hawking followed up with a simplified version, *A Briefer History of Time*.

COMPACT DISCS – 1979

A new medium for the long-playing album

In March 1979, in front of a panel of journalists, a business delegation from the Japanese firm of Sony and the Dutch electronics giant Philips unveiled an ambitious joint venture they were about to launch. The product was a brand-new medium for recorded music rumoured to be so advanced that it would make vinyl records obsolete overnight.

Digital Dire Straits
Mark Knopfler on stage with Dire Straits (above). Their 1985 album Brothers in Arms *was one of the first fully digital recordings and the first CD to sell more than a million copies.*

New generation
The first compact disc player on the market was the Philips CD-100 Magnavox (below), launched in 1982.

The silver, mirror-finish compact disc – CD for short – had several advantages over the vinyl LPs and audio cassettes that it was trying to upstage on the recorded music market. For one thing, it could hold 74 minutes of recorded music, a record at that time. For another, because the songs were all impressed on one side, it was not necessary to turn the disc over half-way through (although not everyone thought this was a plus). It was easy to skip from one track to another and because the reading head of the CD player did not make contact with the playing surface, it was claimed that CDs would not get scratched or worn out.

Music lovers' medium

This new music medium was the culmination not only of a long, difficult programme of technical research and development, but also of protracted business negotiations between the two companies involved. Sony and Philips wanted to avoid the kind of technological war that had pitted them against each other in the battle of the video formats, VHS and Betamax, that ended with the demise of the latter (the Sony product). The Japanese firm had better technical expertise in the digital formatting of music, while the Dutch contributed superior know-how in laser readers. The engineers Kees Schouhamer Immink and Toshitada Doi headed up the research team. An agreement on technical standards governing the development and manufacture of the CD was signed in 1980. Manufacturing licences were granted the following year, and the first CD players appeared in the shops in 1982. Initially, these were very expensive and fewer than 200 albums (most of them classical) were available in the new format.

At first, then, CDs were the preserve of a select band of cognoscenti. They delivered an extremely clean sound that resulted from the new digital recording methods: musical signals were sampled – that is to say, broken down into a series of minuscule, regular time slots – with each sample being digitised. On audio CDs the sampling rate is 44.1 KHz, meaning that each 'sample' of music

A FAILED VENTURE

Although CDs set new standards of crystal clear sound, many audio enthusiasts remained wedded to LPs, claiming that mid-register signals and treble were more precise on vinyl. In response, in 1999 Sony and Philips launched the Super Audio CD, which had around the same storage capacity as a DVD (4.7 GB) and a sampling rate 64 times better than a normal audio CD. But these improved CDs failed to take off in a market that was soon to become dominated by compressed MP3 audio files, downloaded from the Internet. In a world that valued convenience more than quality of sound, few people were prepared to invest in the expensive hi-fi equipment needed to get the best from Super Audio discs.

Down but not out

From the mid-1980s, the racks in music stores filled with CDs, displacing vinyl LPs which most people thought were on their way out for good. But vinyl staged a comeback, emerging as the favoured recording medium of electronic dance and hip-hop artists, as well as club DJs who could do far more with tactile vinyl than they could with the hands-off CD.

is read 44,100 times per second. In this way digital recording captures and encodes the subtleties of tone, pitch and volume. An error-correction system devised by Sony ensured that any errors in reading the disc during playback were automatically rectified. Distortion, extraneous noise and other interference, so common on records and tapes, was virtually eliminated. But some people are hard to please: some music buffs accused the CD sound of being too perfect and lacking the authenticity of the original music as heard on vinyl.

Taking off

Compact discs finally took off in 1985, with the release of the album *Brothers in Arms* by Dire Straits. By then, the cost of CD players had been falling steadily and sales were on the increase. But the remarkably crisp sound of Mark Knopfler's intricate guitar playing – one

of the first performances to be recorded, mixed and transferred digitally (denoted by 'DDD' on the CD label) – finally convinced the buying public that the future belonged to CDs. Despite the fact that they were half as expensive again as cassettes, and that at the time there was no way of copying music onto them at home, music fans flocked to replace their existing vinyl collections on the new medium, as well as seeking out new recordings on CD.

Sales of CD players, initially stand-alone but later incorporated into stereo systems, soared. Over time, the catalogue of artists available on CD grew to embrace every conceivable genre and style. From 1984, with the launch of the Sony Discman, CDs could even be played on portable personal stereo systems, while the 1990s saw the introduction of the first in-car CD players. By 1990, sales of CDs worldwide had topped the 700 million mark.

NOT SO DURABLE

When CDs were first released, it was claimed they would last for 100 years or more, thanks to the lack of any contact between the reading medium and the playing surface. But subsequent laboratory tests have revised this figure downwards, confirming customer experience: CDs, it emerged, were prone to scratching and oxidation, and actually had a useful life of just over a decade.

CD-ROMs and DVDs

Flushed with the success of the audio CD, in 1985 Philips and Sony introduced a spin-off from the technology aimed at the home computer market: the CD-ROM (read-only memory) for storing images and text files.

Burning a CD

On a blank writable CD-R, when the laser reaches a power of 14 milliwatts (mW), it heats up the dye layer and changes its transparency, burning data permanently onto the disc. On CDs of all types, the track that guides the read-write head of the laser takes the form of a spiral running from the centre to the perimeter of the disc.

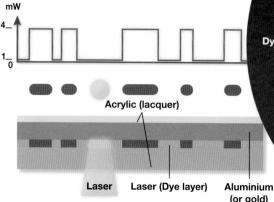

mW

14 —

1 —
0

Acrylic (lacquer)

Laser   Laser (Dye layer)   Aluminium (or gold)

Acrylic layers

Aluminium layer

Dye layer

Offering a storage capacity of 650–700MB, CD-ROMs were reliable and became an instant hit. All PCs began to be fitted with CD drives, supplanting the 3½-inch floppy disks, with what now seemed a puny 1.44MB capacity. CD-ROMs became indispensable computer peripherals for archiving data and an ideal platform for applications, notably video games. In the late 1980s, the first CD burners appeared, which allowed people to archive data on blank recordable CDs (CD-R). A further innovation came in 1990, with the advent of the rewritable CD (CD-RW), enabling users to erase data and re-use the CD. The introduction of rewritable DVDs in 1995 greatly boosted data storage capacity.

Yet even while these new developments were taking place, the rise of the music CD began to tail off. From the start of the new millennium, sales decreased year on year: from 553 million CDs sold worldwide in 2006, the market shrank to 360 million in 2008. The cause was MP3 digital audio files, first developed in the 1990s, which became the preferred way to acquire music in the early 21st century, when sales of MP3 players and Apple iPods soared. The spread of broadband and home computing gave users ready access to music downloads from the Internet. Though the majority of albums sold are still in CD form, this is fast becoming an obsolescent technology as the whole way in which people buy and listen to music changes.

WHAT'S IN A CD?

A CD comprises a thin disc of polycarbonate plastic coated with a microthin layer of reflective aluminium or gold protected by an acrylic lacqeur film. The data is impressed as a series of tiny indentations ('pits'), invisible to the naked eye, in a continuous spiral track moulded into the polycarbonate layer. Each of the pits is between 0.5 and 0.67 microns (one-millionth of a metre) wide and 0.83 and 3.5 microns long, with a minimum depth of 0.2 microns. The arrangement of pits, and the areas between them known as 'lands', corresponds to a digital signal comprised of a succession of zeros and ones – the binary data into which the sound is encoded. The reading head is equipped with a laser diode which projects a beam onto the surface of the disc. When the head is not in contact with a pit, the laser beam is reflected and captured by light-sensitive cells that transform it into a series of electrical pulses. This signal is decoded and amplified to reproduce the sound.

In addition to the layers described above, blank writable CD-Rs have a photosensitive dye layer into which the laser can burn data. On rewritable CDs (D-RW), this layer is replaced by one with a special layer of dye material that can change back and forth between opaque and transparent.

Disc factory

The standard diameter for CDs is 120mm. Many urban myths surround this choice of size, including one that claims it mimicked the diameter of beer mats in Holland.

Data storage
In less than 15 years, CD-ROMs have themselves been supplanted as a data storage method by DVDs, USB memory sticks and external hard drives.

Standard computer kit
From the 1990s onwards, CD-ROMs became the standard method for storing computer data and transferring files. All computers were soon equipped with CD readers and writers.

Sign of the changing times
As an old woman of the Kuna tribe, an Amerindian people living on the San Blas Islands off Panama, embroiders a traditional garment (below), her grandson looks on while listening to music through the headphones of his Discman CD-player.

LOSING CONTROL

When CDs first came on the market, music piracy was not an issue, since people had no means of burning discs at home. But when Napster, an Internet music file-sharing site, began to offer free downloads in the early 2000s, some music publishers responded by applying complex copy prevention systems to the CDs they released. They met limited success: not only could these systems be circumvented (either by downloading special software or using operating systems other than Windows), they also made CDs unplayable on certain systems. Accordingly, EMI and Sony BMG Music Entertainment abandoned copy control in 2006.

Cyclops 1980

The Cyclops system was introduced at the 1980 All-England Tennis Championships at Wimbledon. The brainchild of British-Maltese aero engineer Bill Carlton, it was designed to help umpires determine whether borderline serves were in or out, rather than depending purely on visual judgment. Soon after, it was used at the US and Australian Opens. The system worked by projecting five or six horizontal beams of infrared light 10mm above the court on either side of the service line. These beams converged on a 'magic eye' detector; if a ball fell beyond the service line, breaking a beam, the machine emitted an audible signal. Cyclops had to be activated before each serve by the match umpire, who could overrule the machine. Its accuracy was constantly improved, but in 2007 it was supplanted by the Hawk-Eye system which could operate both for serves and line calls.

Tough call
John McEnroe disputes a line call during his acclaimed match at Wimbledon against the Swede Bjorn Borg in 1980, the year Cyclops was introduced. The system had a margin of error of just 3-4 mm, as compared to 20mm for the human eye.

Renal ultrasound 1980

At the University of Munich in 1975, Professor Walter Brendel, assisted by his colleague Egbert Schmiedt and a student, Christian Chaussy, began research into non-invasive destruction of kidney stones by means of shock waves, now known as lithotripsy. The first patients were treated five

Painless operation
A patient receiving renal ultrasound treatment. The shock waves are acoustic pressure wave pulses that last only a microsecond.

years later in a so-called 'Dornier bath-tub', an early lithotriptor machine in which the patient was partially immersed in water in order to enhance the impact of the shock waves. Lithotriptor machines became widely available from 1984 onwards.

Over a period of about an hour, the patient is subjected to around 4,000–6,000 tiny shocks from high-frequency soundwaves. This shatters the kidney stones, which vary in diameter from 4mm to 20mm, into tiny fragments, which are passed out painlessly through urination. The procedure is now commonplace worldwide.

THE CAVITRON

Patented in 1955 by the Cavitron Equipment Corporation of New York, the Cavitron is an ultrasound device originally designed to help dentists prepare dental cavities prior to filling teeth. After many years of testing, the machine was modified for use by dental hygienists in scaling teeth to remove tartar deposits. The same technology is also applied to destroying brain tumours.

Minitel 1980

In 1975 France began development of the Minitel system, thus becoming the first country to attempt to combine computer and telecommunications technology. The research team, led by Bernard Marti at the National Centre for Telecommunications Studies (CCETT), created a device that linked a small television screen to a telephone network. The interactive teletext that appeared on the screen was produced by a system called Antiope, while a modem and keyboard provided users with an interface via the telephone line to the Transpac data network. Anyone with a telephone line could access the service, which was trialled in 1980 in around 200 homes in several French cities.

Services on tap

Right from the moment it was rolled out nationwide, Minitel proved a huge success. The terminals were distributed free to telephone subscribers and access to the phone directory was also free of charge, but general surfing time was charged at different rates according to the sites visited. A total of more than 20,000 different services were available through Minitel to both private and business users, including train-ticket reservations, weather forecasts, university enrolment, mail-order purchases, banking and even adult chat services.

STILL GOING STRONG

The Minitel system was a major money-spinner for its operator, France Telecom. In 2002 alone, it generated revenues of 845 million euros, via a billion connections to sites from some 5 million terminals. Even in 2010, this pioneering videotex service was still going strong, with around a million terminals in operation, accessing 4,000 services.

Electronic phonebook
A 1980s Minitel advert (inset, above) promoting its most popular service, the free telephone directory. Subscribers accessed the service by keying in '3611'.

In 1994 France Telecom introduced a new terminal that gave users speeds eight times faster than the original, and also offered a version that could transmit photos and documents. At its zenith in 1995, more than 9 million terminals were in operation. The rise of the far more divers Internet has impacted on Minitel, but not as yet entirely eclipsed it. It is still widely used for certain services, notably banking, which benefits from the system's good track record in security.

Students' resource
From 1987, Minitel offered many services later associated with the Internet, including messaging, file sharing and news digests. Students even used Minitel to coordinate a nationwide strike in 1986 (above).

43

Post-it® notes 1981

Evolving brand

After branching out from its original yellow into a wide variety of colours, the Post-it® then took on different shapes – round, square, long and thin, star-shaped. They also became a popular promotional giveaway, as companies printed them with their logos.

In 1968, while trying to develop a super-resistant adhesive, two researchers at the American 3M Corporation (originally the Minnesota Mining and Manufacturing Company), Spencer Silver and Jesse Kops, accidentally came up with the opposite – a formula for a 'low-tack' glue, which was pressure-sensitive and non-permanent. For five years, Silver tried to interest his colleagues in his invention, but with little success. Then, in 1974, another 3M scientist, Art Fry, who had attended a seminar given by Silver, took up the idea. Fry sang in his church choir and found the adhesive particularly useful for sticking place-markers on the pages of his hymn book.

An eye for an idea

Art Fry with a Post-it® stuck to his forehead in his former office at 3M (left). Now that the patent rights on the famous Post-it® have entered the public domain, other companies have rushed to copy the invention and grab a piece of the market for self-adhesive, repositionable office stationery.

At the end of another three years of development work, 3M had devised little blocks of removable notelets with a strip of Silver's glue at the top: the Post-it® was born.

Success at last

The secret of its success lay in the composition of the low-tack glue. It was made from tiny, indestructible acrylic spheres that would stick only where they were tangent to a surface, rather than flat up against it. As a result, the adhesive's grip was sufficiently strong to stick papers together but weak enough to allow them to be pulled apart again without tearing. Even better, the notes could be re-used up to 200 times before losing their adhesion.

Post-it® notes were launched in 1977, but at first customers did not realise how useful they were, so the following year 3M handed out free samples and the product took off. More than 90 per cent of people who tested them expressed satisfaction. 3M patented the product in 1981. Since then, a trillion of these handy little notelets are estimated to have been used in over 100 countries, all manufactured at two plants, one in the USA and one in France.

THE VIRTUAL POST-IT®

The first system of virtual notes was 'Stickies', developed between 1991 and 1993 by Jens Alfke for the Apple computer corporation. In 1995 3M licensed a digital spin-off version of its original paper Post-it® note – Post-it® Software Notes, an application that allowed users to post note-like windows on screen as reminders. These could carry text, hypertext links and e-mail addresses, as well as images of up to 350 pixels.

Solar-powered aircraft 1981

In the late 20th century weird and wonderful flying machines of a style more usually associated with the early days of aviation started to make a comeback. The American engineer Paul MacCready designed and built a plane powered solely by the muscles of the pilot, who operated a set of pedals to turn the propeller. His *Gossamer Condor* made a successful maiden test flight in 1977, then on 12 June, 1979, it crossed the Channel in 2 hours 49 minutes with Bryan Allen, an experienced cyclist, at the controls. MacCready then set about building an aircraft that replaced pedal-power with solar energy gathered by photovoltaic panels mounted on the plane's wings. On 7 July, 1981, his *Solar Challenger* crossed the Channel in the course of a 260km flight from Cormeilles, near Paris, to Manston airfield in Kent. The aircraft flew at a top speed of almost 48km/h and a maximum altitude of over 3,000m.

Closer to the sun

Many imitators followed in MacCready's wake. Solar-powered craft became steadily less dependent on human effort. Wings were made larger to accommodate more solar panels and batteries were installed to store electrical energy. The most remarkable machine of all was *Helios*, an ultralight, remote-controlled flying wing developed by NASA in 2001. With a wingspan of 73.25m – that's greater than the winspan of a Boeing 747 – it can reach 32km/h and has an altitude ceiling of 30,000m to exploit maximum sunlight. The current it stores during the day enables it to keep flying at night. *Helios* is a highly cost-effective 'atmospheric satellite' that performs surveillance and communications duties. It is unmanned; a long-distance solar-powered plane that can carry a pilot and passengers has yet to be invented.

Sun seeker
Helios *photographed on 14 July, 2001, on its inaugural flight over the Pacific Ocean (above). NASA conceived this lightweight drone as the prototype of an aircraft that could stay aloft indefinitely and act as a platform for altitude research projects.*

Making history
Solar Challenger, *the world's first exclusively solar-powered aircraft, taking off from Cormeilles aerodrome near Paris on a test flight on 14 June, 1981. The monoplane weighed a mere 90kg. Its wings, spanning 14m, were fitted with 16,128 photovoltaic cells generating around 3,000 watts.*

THE *SOLAR IMPULSE*

The *Solar Impulse*, a solar-powered plane designed for long-range flight, made its first short 'hop' from Dübendorf airfield in Switzerland on 3 December, 2009. Inaugurated in 2003, the project involved a team of 65 people under the auspices of the Lausanne Federal Technical College and led by André Borschberg and Bertrand Piccard, grandson of the famous adventurer Auguste Piccard, who in 1931 set a world altitude record for the time of almost 16,000m in a stratospheric balloon. With a wingspan of 63.4m – similar to that of an Airbus A340 – and four electric motors, the *Solar Impulse* prototype made its first proper maiden flight on 7 April, 2010. There are plans to build a second aircraft with a pressurised cabin for the pilot, with a view to attempting a round-the-world flight in five legs in 2012.

NEW MATERIALS
Fibres of the future

To judge from outward appearance, many manufactured goods – be they cars, bicycles or socks – have scarcely changed since they were first invented. But in actual fact, the traditional materials that many items were once made of have, over the years, been replaced by entirely new materials that have some remarkable properties.

Essential maintenance
A NASA technician (right) replaces damaged ceramic tiles on the heatshield of the space shuttle Columbia *after its return from its 13th mission. The importance of an intact heatshield cannot be overstated: on* Columbia's *28th mission, an accidental shock damaged the heatshield, causing the shuttle to break up during re-entry.*

In 1991 the legendary tennis player and five-times Wimbledon champion Björn Borg made a comeback after six years' absence from the game – and was blasted off the court. Admittedly, he had not been in training like a top athlete, but the scale of his defeats was still shocking. He lost all of his matches, even against second-rank players. At 35 he was still a relatively young man and just a few years before had been unbeatable, but now he looked like he came from another era. In fact, it was his equipment that was so far out of date. Borg was still playing with a wooden raquet against opponents who were using state-of-the-art ones made from composite materials.

The replacement of traditional materials like wood and metal in the manufacture of a variety of everyday items – from window frames to sports goods and car parts – began in the mid 20th century. Indeed, many products owed their very existence to new materials: without semiconductors, for example, there could have been no computers, while lithium-ion batteries were vital in developing the mobile phone. The advantages of these new materials were legion – not only were they generally lighter, they also brought other beneficial properties, such as being fireproof, anti-microbial, self-cleaning, non-stick, photovoltaic and more.

Alloys, doping and other innovations

The most direct method of making innovative materials was to create new molecules. This harked back to the first generation of plastics and artificial fibres derived from oil in the early 20th century. But by now chemistry had moved on, enabling scientists to alter the microscopic structure of any given substance. Indeed, materials that the layman might assume to have a homogeneous composition are actually made up of minuscule particles or fibres invisible except under a microscope. Modifying the make-up of these molecular or atomic aggregates meant radically altering their properties. In effect, this was what blacksmiths had unwittingly been doing since antiquity, in 'tempering' metals in order to harden them.

In modern chemistry, materials such as metals or ceramics are first broken down into a powder comprising particles or fibres of the desired form, then reconstituted into a solid

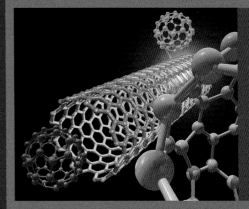

FASCINATING FULLERENES

An artificially produced allotrope of carbon, with molecules of 60 atoms arranged in the shape of a soccer ball, was discovered in 1985 by the physicists Harold Kroto, Robert Curl and Richard Smalley. Named 'buckminsterfullerene' because of its spherical form resembling the geodesic domes of the architect Buckminster Fuller, it is also known as 'fullerene' for short or, colloquially, 'buckyball'. Carbon atoms in their natural state form either hexagonal rings like chicken-wire (graphite) or a cubic crystalline structure (diamond). The two forms of fullerene (left) – buckyballs and 'nanotubes' – are expensive and difficult to produce, but have many applications in medicine and electronics.

material through a process known as 'sintering' (heating under high pressure). This method is used, for instance, to manufacture heat-resistant ceramic tiles such as those that protect space shuttles, or to make tungsten-carbide, an extremely hard compound used to form the heads of drill bits and other machine tools for metalworking, as well as in abrasives.

BIOCOMPATIBLE MATERIALS

There is one major problem associated with medical implants and prostheses: they are made from materials foreign to the organism they are being put into and therefore run the risk of rejection. Since the late 1990s, medical research laboratories have been looking into so-called biocompatible materials, based on polymers more akin to those found in living organisms – such as starch, for example – onto which are grafted chemical radicals selected for particular properties. So far this has led to implants that steadily release medication precisely at the point where it is required and to devices like cardiac valves and semiporous membranes. Researchers are now working on an even more ambitious project aimed at enabling damaged organs to regrow, spurred by the implant of lattices made from biocompatible material that will gradually be colonised by the remaining cells and stimulate the growth of new tissue. These 'smart' matrices give off chemical signals mimicking those naturally occurring in the body in order to attract cells and trigger their multiplication.

Materials are also altered through the controlled addition of impurities to a classic material. Steel is a prime example of the alloying process, whereby a small proportion of another material – such as carbon or tungsten – is introduced according to the property required, such as tensile strength, corrosion resistance and so on. Similarly, microelectronic components and light-sensitive windows or lenses are 'doped' through the addition of a few foreign atoms – in the former by adding phosphorus, arsenic, boron or gallium to silicon, in the latter by adding silver and a halogen, such as iodine, to glass.

If a material is not fit for purpose, it can always be combined with another to make a composite. The earliest instance of this, dating back to Roman times, was the creation of concrete from sand and cement. Modern composites generally comprise a framework of fibres – for example, fibreglass, carbon fibre or Kevlar® – embedded in an amorphous matrix such as a polymer resin. The properties of the whole material often amount to far

Flameproof fabric
A textile called Nomex® was developed by DuPont™ for use in protective clothing worn by firemen and racing drivers. The material is light and does not melt; it only begins to break down at temperatures in excess of 400°C.

Hard honeycomb
A composite material in the form of a honeycomb (below) is both extremely light, due to its open latticework structure, and incredibly rigid, since it distributes weight over a large surface area.

more than the sum of the parts, since the interaction at the point where the two constituent elements join can play a vital role.

Reactive materials

Some high-performance materials are able to pick up an external signal – from temperature, light or mechanical effort, for instance – and react to it. There are shape-memory alloys (SMA), for example, that react to changes in temperature, or piezoelectric materials (ceramics and polymers) that generate a small electric current when they are subjected to pressure. One key use for piezoelectric materials is to detect hairline fractures or unusual stresses in structures such as aircraft cabins. Magnetostrictive materials change shape under the influence of a magnetic field. Researchers are also currently investigating thermoelectric materials, which emit an electric current when they are heated. Even more remarkable is the plan to develop self-repairing materials.

New directions in the auto industry

The year 1972 saw the introduction of the first plastic car bumpers, replacing heavy stainless-steel fenders with rubber buffers. Now customarily made from glass fibre and polyethylene composite materials, bumpers deform and absorb shock on impact, making them far less dangerous to pedestrians. Whatever the mode of transport, weight is the enemy as it increases fuel consumption and pollution. Hence the idea of supplanting steel (in cars and boats) and aluminium (in aircraft) with lighter materials with the same mechanical qualities.

Springing back
One of the most familiar applications of shape-memory alloys is in spectacle frames made from Flexon®, a titanium alloy that is light and extremely flexible.

Mixed materials
Thermoplastic resins are now replacing composite materials in the manufacture of car bumpers and grilles. On this Peugeot 307 (below), only the headlamps are still made from a composite material known as BMC (Bold Molding Compound), a polyester resin with fibreglass.

In 1984 the Renault Espace people-carrier broke new ground in car manufacturing through the use of composite bodywork panels, which cut the vehicle's weight by a third. Certain sections of cars, such as the 'safety cage' passenger compartment and the chassis, must be strong enough to resist crumpling in an accident and so are still made of metal, yet even this could change with the advent of composites based on a carbon fibre skeleton. Carbon fibre is too expensive for large-scale use in volume car production, but this light, rigid and incredibly shock-resistant

INTELLIGENT CEMENT

Bridges, dams and other structures are constantly prey to unseen forces, such as subsidence, traffic loads, vibration, wind and frost. These stresses and strains may create miniature cracks – microfissures – which over time can weaken a structure and even cause sudden collapse, especially in the event of a major earth tremor. Stress can be monitored through the use of probes, but their effectiveness is limited by the impossibility of knowing exactly where fissures will occur. A new 'intelligent' cement may be about to transform this. Ultrafine strands of carbon fibre, several centimetres long, are set in normal cement, giving the material a mild electrical conductance. This enables contractors to measure the electrical resistance all over the building. Any divergence from previous readings indicates either that the structure has been subject to some change, such as a crack, or to mechanical stress.

307 Sedan

material is used in speedboats, in Formula-1 racing cars, in aircraft – the wings of the new super-jumbo Airbus A380, for example – and in spacecraft. Panels of polycarbonate with a durable anti-scratch coating have also begun to displace glass for large glazed areas in buildings as it is half the weight.

Towards the 'smart' house?

Forthcoming innovations in house-building technology include windows that darken automatically in the sun, carpets that eliminate bacteria, walls that absorb or release moisture depending on ambient humidity levels and that can actively filter out outside noise. And all this without the aid of computers, or special control systems or additional work, solely as a

Introducing new mod cons
New materials are finding increasing use in the home. Corian® is an easy-care reconstituted stone widely used for kitchen worktops and sinks (below) and even for furniture and house façades. SentryGlass® laminated windows, seen here (right) on a shopping mall in Florida, are designed to be durable enough to resist hurricane damage.

result of revolutionary materials. Self-cleaning windows, paints, even cements doped with titanium oxide are already a reality: for example, the Dives in Misericordia Church in Rome, consecrated in 2003, has an external coating that keeps the exterior white despite the ravages of air pollution in the city.

Clothing of the future

Since the introduction of synthetic fibres, some articles of clothing have been experiencing an ongoing evolution. From the 1980s, the lives of firemen, mountaineers and all kinds of outdoor sports enthusiasts have been improved by the development of Gore-Tex®, a fabric patented in 1969 that is made waterproof yet breathable through the insertion of a thin, porous membrane of Teflon.

The early 2000s saw the introduction of antibacterial socks to reduce foot odour (the fabric is doped with titanium oxide), entirely crease-resistant fabrics and textiles that respond to changes in temperature. Researchers are busy working on other remarkable types of clothing, including tracksuits that can monitor physical factors such as body temperature or heart rate and adjust their warmth and breathability to make the athlete more comfortable. Armed forces are taking a close interest in camouflage-wear that can change colour with the surrounding environment.

White sails
The Dives in Misericordia Church in Rome (below), designed by the American architect Richard Meier, is a striking example of the use of new materials. For its construction, the Italcementi company devised their Bianco TX Millennium® cement, containing photocatalytic particles that oxidise and destroy organic air pollutants such as exhaust fumes and industrial emissions, so keeping the building gleaming white.

HI-TECH BODY ARMOUR

In 1965 two researchers at the DuPont™ textile concern, Stephanie Kwolek and Herbert Blades, discovered a polymer of benzene and aramid that proved to be incredibly strong and high-tensile. The company patented its new fibre as Kevlar®, with marketing commencing in 1971. Kevlar now has many applications, from use in tyres and aircraft parts to cables for suspension bridges. Perhaps its most famous use is in bullet-proof vests (below), which are more versatile and comfortable than their bulky steel-lined predecessors.

INVISIBLE CLOTHES?

One modern trend in theoretical physics is to try to create coatings that will render objects invisible. These so-called 'metamaterials' – special composites comprising at least one metallic element, with the other usually some kind of glass fibre – involve the application of micrometric or nanometric technology. When subjected to an electromagnetic field, such materials have a negative refractive index, that is, they bend light in the 'opposite' direction to normal materials. At present, the technology is being studied with an eye to creating 'stealth' military equipment invisible to radar, but it is not too fanciful to imagine a kind of 'cloak of invisibility' that would deflect any light rays falling upon it around itself, rather like water flowing either side of a rock in a stream.

The invisible man – almost
Susumu Tachi, professor of physics at Tokyo University, has devised a form of camouflage clothing using a revolutionary material called 'retro-reflectum'. A special camera generates a 3-D image of what is behind the wearer and projects the scene onto the clothing.

Like water off a duck's back
Gore-Tex® fabric is impermeable to rain yet allows condensation from inside a garment to escape. This apparent contradiction is achieved by having micropores 20,000 times smaller than a water droplet, but seven times larger than a molecule of water vapour.

The problem of recycling

Increasingly, the lifespan of products is taken into account when they are first conceived. Certain new materials pose a real problem where recycling is concerned. Ideally, with composite materials the skeleton should be detached from the matrix and each disposed of separately, but this is a laborious business. Latterly, materials made from nanoparticles – such as reinforced rubber for inflatables – have come onto the market, raising concerns over what their environmental impact might be when they come to be recycled.

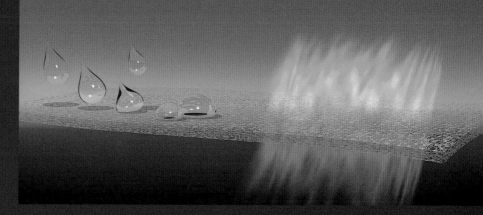

IT where you want it to be

The first portable computers were bulky machines. Initially the term covered both machines that could be carried around but still had to be plugged in to mains electricity and truly portable computers that could run off batteries. Today's laptops have liberated people from the office, affording easy access to remote networks and databases from wherever the user happens to be.

Outwardly, it could almost have been a sewing machine, but the plastic carrying case of the Osborne 1 concealed the ancestor of the modern laptop. When it was launched in 1981 its inventor, the American entrepreneur Adam Osborne, had equipped his brainchild with all the latest technological innovations. It had a processor with a clock frequency of 4MHz and a 64K main memory. Once the machine was laid on its side, the base flipped open to reveal a chunky keyboard and a 5-inch black-and-white cathode-ray screen squeezed in between two full-height floppy disk drives. The machine weighed in at a thumping 10.7kg. An optional battery pack could also be purchased, but the machine was primarily intended to be run on mains power. By today's standards the Osborne 1 was unquestionably bulky, but it was still the world's first piece of IT equipment that allowed people to work away from the office, and it was a great success when it first came out.

Within barely two years big companies such as IBM, Epson, NEC and Compaq had entered the lucrative portable market. Many of the machines produced during this period were unwieldy mini-monsters scarcely or not at all compatible with IBM PCs, the most widely used computer of the day. An exception was the GriD Compass 1101 (1982), designed by the British industrial designer Bill Moggridge for the Grid Systems Corporation based in Silicon Valley, which featured an innovative clamshell screen that folded down over the keyboard when it was being transported. The drawback was the price; at close to $9,000 dollars – around £17,000 at current values – only major corporations and agencies like NASA could afford it.

The first truly portable computer was the Toshiba T1100, which appeared in 1985. It weighed just over 4kg, was IBM-compatible

Nearly man
Adam Osborne (right) with a prototype of the Osborne 2 portable in 1983.

EARLY MARKET LEADER

The reasonable price tag on the Osborne 1 portable computer – $1,795, with $1,500 of software thrown in free – assured it a ready market. Tens of thousands were sold in the first two years, taking the company from nothing to a monthly turnover in excess of a million dollars. Flushed with success, Adam Osborne could not resist announcing the second generation of portable computer – prematurely, as the design was still on the drawing board. Sales plummeted and the company went into liquidation in 1983.

High performance
The GriD Compass 1101 (above) was originally developed for business executives. NASA used them on board space shuttle missions in the 1980s and 90s.

and had 8 hours' running time on its rechargeable battery pack, which finally liberated the portable from the wall socket.

Evolution of the species

While office PCs of this period had hard drives, the first portables could only use their built-in ROM (read-only memory) as their operating system. Then in 1988 the Compaq SLT/286 appeared, offering mass storage in the form of a 20MB hard disk. Large-format (5¼-inch) floppy disks, then 3½-inch floppies, were supplanted by CD-ROMs in the late 1980s. CD readers and then writers became standard on laptops from the turn of the 21st century.

From the earliest days of portable computers, graphical user interfaces (GUI) began to replace the austere command-line type of interface. Several of these new machines were fitted with a 'trackball' to enable users to navigate around the screen; a mouse was an optional extra, but still prohibitively expensive. The first portable to incorporate a touchpad was the Gavilan SC (1984); a decade later Apple's PowerBook 500 established the touchpad as the standard navigational device on laptops. The joystick in the middle of the keyboard, used by IBM on its 1992 ThinkPad, never caught on.

Screen technology came on in quantum leaps and bounds. The Commodore SX-64 Portable (1983) pioneered the full-colour screen. The first displays with 256 colours were launched in 1993, with 7 million colours

Filing copy
A row of journalists filing copy to their respective newspapers during the visit of Prince Charles to Russia in May 1994.

Computer fair
A Siemens salesman shows off the company's range of high-performance laptops during IFA 2009, the world's largest trade fair for consumer electronics held annually in Berlin.

New learning
Schoolchildren in China gather round their school's only laptop to watch an animation. Since 2003 China has outstripped Taiwan to become the world's main manufacturer of laptops, after several foreign companies relocated their factories there.

becoming standard by the turn of the century. Portables with plasma screens, introduced in 1988, improved image quality, but had the disadvantage of running the battery down fast. By 1991 they had been supplanted by two new types of liquid-crystal display (LCD): dual-scan STN and TFT. Both gave excellent-quality images while using a minimum of power, but the sharp decline in the cost of TFTs gave them the edge, making them the industry standard.

Reaching full potential

Prior to the 1990s, portable computers were seriously hampered by performance issues. Manufacturers, who had to trade off the

parameters of independent operation and power supply, could not afford to fit laptops with high-performance processors that would drain the battery too quickly. Another consideration was that, as machines became more compact, fast processors tended to generate too much heat within the confined space. The advent of the Intel i386SL microprocessor in 1991, followed by the i486SL, with their sophisticated 'sleep' modes, enabled laptops to conserve battery power while sacrificing none of their capacity. Processor speeds increased from 20MHz in the early 1990s to over 2GHz a decade later.

Microsoft's Windows 95 operating system (1992) had an 'Advanced Power Management' system that could place the CPU (central processing unit) in a low-power state and deactivate the hard drive and CD reader when the computer was in sleep mode. Concurrently, researchers were working on improving battery power. Nickel-cadmium cells were replaced by nickel-metal hydride, then by lithium-ion polymer batteries. Lighter and more efficient, these could run ever more powerful and energy-hungry components while still ensuring several hours of mains-free operation.

Enabling distance working

Laptops became far more widespread in the 1990s as the price came down. Even so, the cost of miniaturising parts and fitting them into

---

DIFFERENT DESIGNATIONS

The term 'portable' covers a range of machines. Ultraportables – small, light, yet powerful laptops – made their first appearance in 1989. They weigh less than 2kg and have a screen of less than 12 inches (measured diagonally). In 2000 these smaller machines gave rise in turn to an even more compact device, the Tablet PC, which has a touch screen (often pivoting) and a stylus pen. The high cost of tablets largely restricted them to business use. Notebooks are the mass-market equivalent – similarly sized but less powerful and equipped with a DVD – introduced into Europe by Asus in 2008. At the other end of the spectrum are 'transportable' computers, which with a screen of up to 17 inches are relatively heavy and intended for moving occasionally rather than carrying everywhere.

an ever smaller space meant that portable computers remained some 20 to 40 per cent more expensive on average than equivalent-specification desktop machines. Moreover, since it was impossible to replace components, they became obsolete in just a few years.

Nevertheless, these disadvantages failed to blight customers' love-affair with the laptop. Its great selling point was the flexibility it gave professionals to work away from their offices – on trains and planes, for example – and to access their files and e-mails from a single, portable workstation. Laptops also promoted the leisure use of the computer as people began to use them to watch feature films, play computer games and store music and photos. Since the introduction of USB ports, laptop users can attach memory sticks, speakers and other peripherals. Webcams, fitted at the top of the screen from the early 2000s, have made video-conferencing easier, while the advent of WiFi connectivity from 1999 onwards provided a further boost to laptop ownership.

Style icons

As laptops grew ever slimmer in the early 2000s, they became style icons of the modern age. Notebooks – lightweight, ultraportable laptops – made their debut in 2008. The most

Ultra-slim
Made from a single block of aluminium and weighing just 1.36kg, the MacBook Air became an instant design classic when it was launched in 2008. Despite its slim dimensions, its processing power and screen resolution outstrip many larger desktop computers.

elegant of this latest generation of ultralight laptops was undoubtedly Apple's MacBook Air, a WiFi notebook less than 2cm thick at its deepest point, but all computer manufacturers have placed a premium on design, with laptops becoming less angular, more user-friendly and available in a range of colours.

In 2008 sales of laptops outstripped those of desktop PCs for the first time. Technological innovations included solid-state hard drives with flash memory which were much quieter and more durable than before, plus DVD Blu-Ray players and HD screens. Laptops incorporating displays with organic light-emitting diodes (OLEDs), which make screen colours incredibly lifelike, are already a reality. Future advances are set to include flexible and touch screens.

Digital education
Several countries have now trialled school computer networks using laptops. This student (top) is using her 'electronic satchel' (Cartable électronique) in a class in France. It gives the student instant access to all kinds of learning resources, such as dictionaries and textbooks. The system also incorporates a chatroom where parents and teachers can interact.

BILL GATES AND STEVE JOBS
Two computer wizards

Bill Gates and Steve Jobs came from very different backgrounds but have much in common. They were both born in 1955 and an early catalyst in both their careers was the Altair 8800, a microcomputer launched in 1975 by Micro Instrumentation and Telemetry Systems (MITS). The Altair marked a turning point in their lives, transforming them from computer hobbyists into professional players. They went on to become the two most famous figures of the IT world, heading up huge multinational corporations.

Going places

Bill Gates in 1986 (right), a big year for the young computer entrepreneur: not only did PC Magazine award him a prize for his pioneering work in the computer industry, but he also floated Microsoft on the US Stock Exchange. At the time registration cost just $21: by the end of the year, aged just 31, Gates was a billionaire.

The introduction of the Altair 8800 proved a catalyst for Bill Gates and his friend Paul Allen, who had been writing computer programs as a hobby ever since attending prep school together in Seattle. Realising that there was an emerging market in creating software for microcomputers, they contacted the president of MITS, Ed Roberts, and showed him a BASIC operating system they had developed over just a few weeks for his Altair machine. Impressed, Roberts hired Allen and bought the rights to the software from Micro-Soft, as the company that Gates and Allen had just founded then styled itself (short for Microcomputer Software). But instead of selling their system outright, which was normal practice at the time, Gates sold Roberts a licence for non-exclusive usage. For for every Altair sold, MITS paid Micro-Soft $35 for the operating system.

Apple enters the fray

In April that same year, 1975, way down the US west coast in Menlo Park, California, the 30 or so members of the 'Homebrew Computer Club' were busy studying the workings of an Altair 8800. Two friends in the club, Steve Jobs and Steve Wozniak, were convinced they could improve on the MITS machine, so they set about building their first computer – the Apple I – in Jobs' garage. They founded Apple

Computer, Inc. on 1 April, 1976. Because they knew that kit-form computers would only ever appeal to enthusiasts, their first priority was to create a ready-assembled computer for the mass market. This machine, the Apple II, was launched in 1977 after the company had set up its headquarters at Cupertino (California), where it remains to this day.

Mr Microsoft

William Henry Gates III came from a privileged background and was enrolled at the exclusive Lakeside School in Seattle in 1968 when he was 13 years old. The school had just entered into an agreement to buy its pupils computer time on a minicomputer belonging to a local company, the Computer Center Corporation (CCC). Young Bill became fascinated by this machine and learned how to program it in BASIC. He spent so many hours doing this that the school excused him from maths lessons.

A few months later, Bill and his friend Paul Allen along with two other boys were banned by the company from using the computer for exploiting bugs to get free computer time. When they were allowed back in, they offered to correct the bugs in the software, in the process studying source code for the various programs that ran on the machine. Though Bill Gates was still not yet 15, he proceeded to write a program for the school to schedule its lessons. In 1972, aged 17, he and Allen founded the Traf-O-Data company, which made traffic counters. The following year, he went to Harvard University, where he further broadened his interest in computer science.

With the launch of Altair BASIC in 1975, Bill Gates established Micro-Soft with financial

---

THE MICROSOFT MILLIONAIRE

Paul Allen was two years older than Bill Gates and working as a programmer at Honeywell in Boston before he and Gates founded Microsoft. He quit the company in 1983 for health reasons, but he continued to invest in financial markets and telecommunications. Although he was a less flamboyant figure than Gates, he still became a multimillionaire in his own right.

Business brain and benefactor
The two sides of Bill Gates: business magnate and head of the world's leading computer software company (right, in 1998), and philanthropist (above), photographed with Malaysian orphans at the new township of Cyberjaya in 2000. Cyberjaya and its science park were created with Microsoft aid to attract IT and telecommunications firms to relocate there.

support from his family. He soon proved to have ruthless business acumen, always seeking to establish a monopoly in the markets he was involved in. Years later, both the US Congress (in 2000) and the European Commission (2004, 2006, and 2008) would find Microsoft guilty of breaching antitrust regulations and stifling competition, but this had little effect.

Microsoft really took off in 1980 when IBM was looking for an operating system for the personal computer it was developing. Bill Gates purchased a system called QDOS from a small firm called Seattle Computer Products, adapted it to the PC, renamed it MS/DOS, then sold on non-exclusive rights to IBM. From the mid-1980s, as the PC market mushroomed, first other main computer manufacturers and then thousands of smaller assemblers began to offer clones of the IBM PC – and every single one of them was equipped with MS/DOS.

In 1985 Microsoft introduced Windows, a graphical interface for the PC now installed on almost every microcomputer in the world – except those made by Apple. Sold as a bundle comprising a suite of business and home-user programs called Microsoft Office, Windows became Microsoft's flagship product.

In 2000 Gates stepped down as chief executive at Microsoft, handing the role over to Steve Ballmer, while retaining control over strategic policy and new product development. On 27 June, 2008, he quit his full-time role at Microsoft completely, although he remains the company's chairman and principal shareholder. From 1993 onwards, he has been ranked as one of the world's richest men.

A high-handed visionary

Steve Jobs grew up in California as the foster child of a lower-middle-class family after his biological parents put him up for adoption. As a boy, he had a rebellious streak. Aged 13 he became friends with Steve Wozniak, an 18-year-old obsessed with electronics who had already invented a device (a so-called 'blue box') that could generate the necessary tones

The way we were
Steve Jobs (below), the visionary head of Apple, at the press conference in San Francisco launching the iPad on 27 January, 2010. Behind him is a blown-up photograph of himself (on the left) with Steve Wozniak, taken in the garage where they made the Apple I, on 1 April, 1976, the day they estabished the Apple company.

to make long-distance telephone connections without the caller being billed. In 1974, Jobs dropped out of college after only one semester and took a job with the Atari video games company. He left to travel to India in search of spiritual enlightenment, became a Buddhist and, like many of his contemporaries in the counterculture, tried LSD. Back in the States, he rejoined Atari where he worked on a circuit board for a video game. When the Altair 8800 appeared in 1975, Jobs realised that an IT revolution was unfolding. The next year, he founded Apple with Wozniak and Ronald Wayne, another friend.

Jobs was a brilliant visionary, if autocratic and disorganised, while Wozniak was a perfectionist, and the pair formed a fruitful partnership. In 1981, while Wozniak was still tinkering away trying to improve the command-line interface of the Apple II computer, Jobs was convinced that a graphical user interface was the right way to go for the personal computer. And so, on 24 January, 1984, Apple launched the Macintosh, the first in a line of highly innovative and enormously successful computers, as well as other products, that continues to this day. Coupled with a laser printer and page make-up software, the Macintosh laid the foundations of desktop publishing (DTP). Creating niche markets and designing products to fill them became Apple's trademark.

But unlike Bill Gates at Microsoft, Jobs did not have absolute control as head of Macintosh. In May 1985 he was ousted by the new CEO of Apple, John Sculley. He responded by founding NeXT Computer, with the intention of making better products than Macintosh. The result was a technological triumph but a commercial failure. In 1986

Designers' choice
Launched in 1986, the Apple II GS, a higher-spec version of the Apple II, had a 16-colour, 640 x 200 pixel screen and a powerful processor. It soon established itself as the industry standard for graphic and book designers.

Jobs bought the IT division of Lucas Film and founded Pixar Studios. Ten years later, Pixar's *Toy Story* became the first full-length animated feature film to be entirely computer generated and was a huge worldwide hit. Meanwhile, strategic mismanagement by John Sculley and his successors had driven Apple into serious financial difficulties.

When Apple bought NeXT in 1996, Jobs was reabsorbed into the company as a special adviser and soon regained his position as CEO at a symbolic salary of just one dollar (plus stock options and other benefits in kind). After relaunching the company, in 1997 he opened the online Apple Store and introduced the stylishly curved and multicoloured iMac, especially designed for Internet access. Since then, the steady stream of successful and groundbreaking products to emerge from the Apple stable has included the iPod music player (teamed with the iTunes online music store), the iPhone (2007) and the iPad tablet (2010).

Blue-sky thinker
Steve Jobs pictured in 1999 with the new iBook. This was part of a range of beautifully designed and cleverly branded products that earned the Apple Macintosh a loyal following worldwide.

STEVE WOZNIAK

Born in 1950, Steve Wozniak displayed a gift for electronics from an early age. When he was just 13, he put together both a radio ham's transmitter and his own transistorised pocket calculator. In 1971, before meeting Steve Jobs, he and a friend, Bill Fernandez, built a computer they named 'Cream Soda'. After crashing his light plane in 1981, he used his term of sick leave from Apple to complete his unfinished undergraduate degree (in electrical engineering) at the University of Berkeley, under an assumed name. He left Apple for good in 1985 to concentrate on educational and philanthropic projects, focusing especially on promoting technology programs in schools.

New generation

The Apple iPad (right) broke new ground in 2010 by offering the versatility of the iPhone, with its welter of applications or 'apps', in a slim tablet format that also enables users to download and read e-books and online journals.

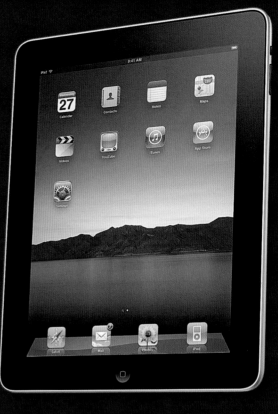

Global crash

In August 2003 the 'Blaster worm' computer virus caused the worst global computer crash to date. The worm spread through Microsoft Windows 2000 and XP operating systems, both of which had proved vulnerable to cyber attack, and wrought brief havoc on the PCs of home and business users alike.

Stormy relations

Since the outset, when Bill Gates' company developed the AppleSoft operating system for the Apple II, the fortunes of Microsoft and Apple have been closely linked. But Microsoft's introduction launch of Windows in 1985, which clearly owed a great deal to the graphical interface pioneered by Macintosh, prompted Apple to take Microsoft to court for copyright infringement. The case dragged on from 1988 to 1994, when Apple finally lost on appeal.

Even so, a new lawsuit was threatened until Jobs took over the company again and reached an out-of-court settlement. Apple agreed to drop the charges in return for Microsoft injecting $150 million of capital into Apple and collaborating on developing versions of Microsoft Office and MS Explorer for the Mac. Peace finally appeared to have broken out between the two IT giants.

Harnessing the wind

Wind has been harnessed since ancient times as the motive force for sailing ships and to drive the sails of windmills. With the advent of wind turbines it found an important new role as a renewable source of energy, offering a way of generating electricity without producing the pollution that comes from fossil fuels.

A head for heights
Regular maintenance and inspection of wind turbines is a hands-on affair undertaken every six months. Depending on their height, masts have a lift or ladders inside. Cleaning and repairing the outside of a turbine has to be done by workers abseiling down from the nacelle (above). Managing the flow of electricity from wind farms and streaming it into the national power grid is done remotely by computerised control centres.

Source of strength
A welder at work inside a wind turbine mast (right). The mast must be immensely strong to support the weight of the rotor and generating equipment, while resisting the force of the wind. Most are built of steel and are 5 metres wide.

Anyone driving to San Francisco on the Interstate 580 freeway cannot fail to notice the strange white forest that looms up around 60 miles east of the city. Here, at the highest point on the Altamont Pass, stand some 4,930 turbine masts, their three-bladed rotors all facing into the prevailing wind. Built in 1981, the same year as a similar facility further south at Tehachapi, this is the oldest wind farm in the world. It still boasts the largest concentration of turbines with a capacity of 576 megawatts (MW), the equivalent of six nuclear reactors.

In search of renewable energy

The first large, three-bladed wind turbine to generate electricity was designed by the Danish engineer Johannes Juul and erected near the town of Gedser in 1957. It operated until 1967, producing an output of 200kW. The Danish experiment remained a one-off until the oil crisis of 1973 sent the price of oil soaring, prompting governments to investigate alternative energy forms. In Denmark this led to the development of the Riisager wind turbines, built between 1976 and 1980. In the USA cooperation between government, NASA and private companies led to the first wind farms being built on the coast of California in the early 1980s. Similar projects were pursued in the Netherlands and West Germany.

In the early 2000s, when governments finally acknowledged the threat posed by climate change, industrial-scale wind turbines started to spring up across the world. On average, a farm of 100 large turbines produces 500MW – about the same as a conventional coal or gas-fired power station, but only about a third of the output of a nuclear plant. The cost per kW of wind-generated electricity cannot compete with that from fossil fuels or nuclear, but it has none of their negative environmental impact. Plus, it compares favourably with other renewables: 1kW

ANATOMY OF A TURBINE

There are three main sections that made up the body of a wind turbine:
The mast: the tall structure that supports the rotor blades and nacelle can vary between 10 and 100 metres in height to catch the optimal airflow for the location.
The rotor: usually with 3 blades – some have 2 – the rotor is driven by the force of the wind.
The nacelle: perched on the opposite side of the mast to the rotor, this houses the electric generator and gearbox, which are connected to the rotor by a drive shaft. The electricity generated can vary from several hundred kilowatts to 5 megawatts.

On horizontal-axis turbines (the most common sort) the rotor blades are set perpendicular to the wind. There are also vertical-axis (or Darrieus) turbines, which are relatively compact and can exploit very light wind, but they yield far less than horizontals.

Bird's eye view
The turbines at Altamont Pass, California (left). The original structures are now being replaced by more modern types that have less impact on bird life.

Wind over water
Thorntonbank offshore wind farm (above), which commenced operations in 2009 with six turbines, is located 20 miles off Zeebrugge and the Belgian coast. Eventually, 60 turbines will stand here, generating a total capacity of 300MW, enough to supply the electricity needs of 600,000 people.

of electricity from wind turbines works out slightly more expensive than its hydroelectric counterpart, but it is only about one-quarter of the cost of the energy generated by solar panels.

An increasing share

Today China heads the list of countries that use wind power as part of their electricity generating programme: in 2010 China had a capacity of 41,800MW – around 5 per cent of its total energy production. Next came the USA with 40,200MW (2.5 per cent of total energy), then Germany with 27,214MW (7 per cent) and Spain with 20,676MW (9 per cent). These figures represent a huge increase from just a few years ago. In total, wind turbines account for some 2 per cent of all the energy generated around the world, but this is set to double by 2012 as more wind farms come on stream. Europe leads the way in offshore wind farms.

With classic horizontal wind turbines now at the peak of their development potential, a step-change in technology will be needed for yield to increase significantly. A number of projects are currently on the drawing board. Engineers are studying the feasibility of radical new airborne turbines operating at altitudes between 1,000 and 10,000 metres to exploit the higher wind speeds there. These future structures will bear little resemblance to the turbines of today – one plan is for a sail-like construction trailing a cable that feeds an alternator; another is for the multi-wing structures being built by Joby Energy in the USA. These kite-like turbines, comprising up to 60 rotors, will fly in circular paths in the upper layer of the atmosphere. Their inventors envisage them generating 50MW by 2020.

AN ILL WIND?

Despite being non-polluting, wind turbines have sparked argument and controversy in some countries. Some people object to them because of their visual impact on the countryside. Another complaint concerns the constant hum of the rotors – though unobtrusive in isolation, an entire farm of turbines can create serious noise pollution, and manufacturers are now working on rotor blades that make less noise. Wind turbines may also impair electromagnetic waves (radio and TV signals) in areas where reception is weak. One solution is to site wind farms offshore, but this greatly increases construction costs.

THE ELECTRONICS AGE
Indispensable and omnipresent

The electronics age really began back in 1904 with the invention of the diode, but it only came into its own with the advent of the integrated circuit and the microprocessor. Since then, electronic goods have become indispensable in our daily lives.

Key breakthrough
The printed circuit board (above right), in varying degrees of complexity, is the keystone of all the myriad electronic devices that have become an integral part of modern life. They are with us from the moment we wake up, in the shape of the digital alarm clock (right).

Perhaps the most eloquent proof of the triumphant march of electronics is the fact that the word is used so indiscriminately these days, far beyond its original narrow definition. While no-one talks about 'chemicals' when they mean medicine, or of 'electrics' in reference to an iron or a hair dryer, people will blithely refer to a computer as an example of 'electronics'. In the strictest sense of the term, electronics simply denotes the study of electrical conduction in vacuums, gases or semiconductors. But in common parlance it has come to signify the huge range of gadgets that today perform ever more complex tasks in ever shorter timespans, while using an increasingly small amount of energy.

In 1904 John Ambrose Fleming invented the thermionic valve, which could detect high-frequency waves such as radio signals. Few people today appreciate that this valve was the direct ancestor of the transistor, in that both of them act as current rectifiers. The fragility and high cost of the valves, also known as vacuum tubes, prompted the US army to commission the American physicist Walter Brattain to seek an alternative, which led to the germanium transistor. It was this invention that truly marked the beginning of the modern era of electronics. Nowadays the popular conception of electronics is epitomised more by devices such as those installed on modern airliners to monitor and collect data on the distance covered, the plane's air speed and fuel reserves and the strength of the headwind, then analyse the findings to advise the pilot on the speed needed to ensure the plane arrives on time. Electronics is also increasingly associated with the gadgets that rule our daily lives, though in fact these owe just as much to advances in automation and information technology.

From watches to MRI scanners

From its inception right up to the birth of the microprocessor – which Gordon Moore, one of the founders of Intel, rightly called 'one of the most revolutionary products in the history of mankind' – the pure science of electronics was the preserve of high-flying engineers. But the introduction of the Intel 4004 processor in 1971 changed the landscape. The Intel 4004 offered the same processing power as the colossal pioneering ENIAC computer – which took up a whole room with its array of cabinets and 18,000 vacuum tubes – but could be held in the palm of the hand. It had 2,250 transistors arranged in four separate circuits, enabling it to carry out 60,000 operations per second. In terms of size, speed and reliability it heralded a whole new era in computing.

At $200 per microprocessor, the Intel 4004 was expensive for the time, but NASA, which had a virtually insatiable demand, ordered so many that the price quickly began to fall. Even so, most people at the time could scarcely have imagined the scale of its future applications. In 1972 Intel announced the successor to the

---

DIGITAL VERSUS ANALOGUE

When radio and later television first came on the scene, all transmission was by means of analogue signals, which use sound or light waves in their original form. Digital signals, which are increasingly being used by broadcasters, transmit the data in binary code and take up far less bandwidth. In television, for example, digital multiplexing enables broadcasters to transmit several channels simultaneously over the same frequency channel. In addition, digital signals are less susceptible to fading or interference.

Aids to air safety

Advances in electronics have given air-traffic controllers – llike these men (above) in the control tower at New York's John F. Kennedy Airport – powerful new tools to help in their vital role. Improvements in radar and radio technology allow a growing volume of air traffic to be safely managed by day or night and whatever the weather.

4004 – the 8008. This was to become the core of the first microcomputer to be sold fully assembled (albeit without keyboard or hard disk): the French Micral-N in 1973.

Meanwhile, things were stirring in the wider consumer goods market: the first electronic digital watch, named the Pulsar, made its debut in the USA at the astronomical price of $2,000. The first pocket calculators, made by Hewlett-Packard and Texas Instruments, began to appear in 1972, although they were so bulky by today's standards they barely justified their name. Here, too, before economies of scale kicked in to drive down the price, few people could afford them.

Video games would soon become the next big thing in electronics: Microsoft, for example, introduced Flight Simulator for trainee pilots in 1982. That same year the camcorder and video player gave the general public the ability to record movies and play them back instantly.

HOW TO SPEAK TO A MACHINE

In order to instruct a machine how to perform any given task, it is first necessary to give it a method – namely an algorithm. Each algorithm can be broken down into a sequence of simple operations, which are programmed into the machine's electronic circuits. This task lies within the domain of information technology, which has evolved hand-in-hand with electronics.

Home help

Modern washing machines (below) are pre-programmed to wash, rinse and spin loads for different lengths of time and at varying temperatures to suit different fabrics. Some washer-dryers switch automatically into drying mode after the wash cycle.

This technology became the battleground between two rival video formats: Sony's Betamax and JVC's VHS. The 1980s also saw a boom in electronically controlled domestic appliances, with the advent of programmable fridges, cookers and automatic washing machines. The world of motoring began to change, too, as automatic fuel injection, braking systems and electronic key fobs became standard in cars. Heavy goods vehicles and coaches were fitted with speed governors, which make the accelerator increasingly hard to press down as the vehicle approaches the pre-programmed maximum speed.

Medicine also benefited. Semiconductors played a key role in the development of two invaluable diagnostic instruments: the electrocardiograph (ECG) for measuring electrical activity in the heart and the electroencephalogram (EEG) which monitors brain waves. Medical imaging across a range of techniques – CT scans, magnetic resonance spectroscopy (MRS), magnetic resonance imaging (MRI), scintigraphy, endoscopy – was improved beyond recognition by the application of microelectronics.

Finally, alarm systems, whether for homes or businesses, became far more sophisticated through the use of infrared sensors that could instantly detect intruders and alert security personnel to intercept them.

A perfectly controlled world

Industry has been a major beneficiary of the electronics revolution. Computer-controlled production lines have become the norm across the whole gamut of manufactured goods, from electric light bulbs to engines, from canned food to sheet metal. The automobile industry was an early adopter of the technology, with centralised computer systems managing assembly lines of robots welding car bodies.

Broadly speaking, electronics splits into two main areas: on the one hand, standalone equipment such as video cameras or washing machines; and on the other hand, large systems that monitor ebb and flow in real time in a variety of different domains, such as air, rail and road traffic, weather patterns, gas or

Going digital
Stock markets computerised in the 1980s. In the process they became sources of real-time financial information.

Instant information
Electronic screens are now standard at airports (below), providing information on arrivals and departures and allowing passengers to check the gate number and boarding status of their plane without the need to seek assistance.

DATA COMPRESSION

Most current modems download data at a rate of 56,000 bits per second (bps). But in 2008, the US telecommunications company AT&T Paradyne introduced a data compression system that could transmit TV signals to mobile phones at a rate of 1.5 to 2 million bps.

Digital democracy
Electronic voting booths in Miami in use during the 2004 presidential election. The incumbent President, George W. Bush, won a second term in office, beating off a challenge from the Democratic candidate John Kerry.

electricity distribution and stock-market information, to name just a few. In such systems a computer gathers data, sometimes from hundreds or thousands of miles away – meteorological data from a weather satellite, for example – then processes it and feeds it through to other computers.

If the capacity of a particular venue is restricted by safety regulations, a computer can, in real time, calculate the number of people who have come through a turnstile and automatically prevent more people entering. Or if traders in New York wish to see how

certain share prices are faring in Tokyo or on the London or Frankfurt markets, a simple program can highlight relevant share prices on their computer screens – in red for a falling price, green for a rising one. Likewise, computer-controlled signals automatically alert staff at local electricity substations if consumption is approaching the limits of capacity. And the central computer in an air traffic control unit can give advance warning of severe weather, enabling flights to be diverted or put on hold in good time.

Monitoring systems may sometimes be extremely fine-tuned. Take, for example, the case of a person trying to use a cash machine. Customers are usually allowed three attempts at putting in their correct pin, but two errors in entering the PIN followed by an attempt to withdraw a larger sum than an average transaction will automatically trigger some systems to block the withdrawal, even if sufficient funds are available, on the grounds that the card may have been stolen. Similarly, in cases of hostile company takeover bids, specially mandated city traders may intervene to block speculation involving the stock of a particular company through the installation of a program that instantly buys up all available shares as soon as their price begins to fall.

Electronic downside
Toxic metals and chemicals, such as lead and dioxins, are used in some computer components. There is a risk that these will damage the health of poor people in the developing world who scavenge rubbish tips for a living, like these boys in Ghana, one of the countries to which machines discarded in the West are often shipped.

High speed on the rails

In the 30 years of its existence, the TGV – *Train à grande vitesse*, or 'high-speed train' – has revolutionised rail travel in Europe. By putting formerly far-flung regions in easy contact with one another, the high-speed rail network has helped to stimulate economic regeneration. Today, the TGV and its counterparts elsewhere offer a viable alternative to short-haul flights.

Train of the future
Passengers being served a meal on an early TGV. Jacques Cooper, the man who conceived both the train's external profile and interior décor, was given the brief to design 'a train that doesn't look like one'.

On 22 September, 1981, the TGV Number 16 slipped out of the station at Mâcon in eastern France, watched by a crowd of journalists and onlookers. Its departure was heralded by a violent rainstorm. In the cab, the French president François Mitterrand sat listening closely as the driver explained the train's controls. Outside, the rain began to bucket down so hard it caused a power failure. Scarcely out of the station, the train lost all its momentum and instead of surging to the expected 200km/h, it merely trundled along at a sedate 90km/h. Then, as power was restored, the TGV showed what it could do on the downhill stretch that followed, accelerating up to 260km/h. The inauguration of the first

French high-speed railway line, from Paris to Lyons, had turned out to be a great success. In France and abroad, the TGV's maiden run grabbed the headlines. Among the commentators, there were more than a few who realised that this low-slung, orange train heralded a new era in railway transport.

The Japanese model

By the time the TGV first took to the rails, the Japanese had long since provided a model for modern high-speed rail travel. As early as 1959 it was decided to construct a high-speed line from Tokyo to Osaka, with an eye to the Winter Olympics that were to be held in Japan in 1964. The general operating speed was set at 210km/h. The new line brought the journey time down from nine hours to just three hours ten minutes. At the time, the country was at the height of its post-war economic boom, and embarked on expanding the costly high-speed project without more ado. Modernising Japan's rail infrastructure meant starting from scratch, as the existing lines were far too winding to take trains of any appreciable speed. Over the course of the 1960s Japan saw the appearance

of a whole new generation of streamlined trains known as *Shinkansen*; the Japanese term simply means 'new trains,' but the world came to know them colloquially as 'bullet trains'. They were comfortable, safe and punctual, and became an instant hit with commuters.

European state railway companies took a close interest in the Japanese developments. In the mid-1960s, France's SNCF and Germany's Deutsche Bahn (DB) realised that long-distance train travel was coming under increasing competition from short-haul flights. Extrapolating from this trend, they predicted that before long the train would only be used for commuting from the suburbs to city centres, or dwindle to serving at most mid-distance or unpopular destinations. This spurred them into action. In 1965 DB instituted an experimental service, running at 200km/h, between Munich and Augsburg. In France SNCF increased the

speed on its existing tracks to 200km/h, as the maximum permissible speed for conventional locomotives and rolling stock. But in order to really give the burgeoning airlines a run for their money, speeds would have to increase to 250 or even 300km/h. Neither the existing locomotives nor the railbed and tracks, some of which dated back to the mid-19th century, could sustain such speeds. The French authorities decided to bite the bullet and follow the Japanese example: they embarked on the CO3 project, which would culminate in the launch of the TGV 15 years later.

Paris to Lyons in two hours

The first plan that French engineers came up with was for an aerotrain service with trains running on an air cushion, like a tracked hovercraft. This was followed by plans for a gas-turbine powered train (see box above).

In the hot seat
President François Mitterrand (above left) and the French transport minister in the driver's cab on the TGV's maiden run in September 1981.

Speeding south
These twin viaducts carry the TGV lines across the River Rhône near Avignon.

Motive power
An engineer working on the coils of a new electric motor for a TGV train. A power input of 25,000 volts is required to run these engines.

The project to build a high-speed line for turbotrain services from Paris to Lyons was approved in 1974, but with the developing oil crisis in the mid-1970s SNCF shelved the technology and resorted to the more traditional solution of overhead electric traction. The Alstom company built a single electric railcar unit called the Zebulon Z 7001 to test engines for what would be the TGV and also a new type of bogie (the trolley under the train, on which are mounted the axles and wheels) designed for high-speed operation. Between 1974 and 1978, this prototype covered 685,000km at an average speed of 300km/h.

Construction of the 426km Paris–Lyons high-speed line began in 1976, the first new line

FAST TRAINS IN GERMANY

The German railway network began running high-speed trains a decade after France's pioneering TGV. The first scheduled InterCity Express (ICE) trains were from Hamburg in the north to Munich in the south, via Frankfurt and Stuttgart. The latest generation of these trains can run at speeds of up to 320km/h. But in 1998, seven years after its inception, Germany's high-speed network suffered a terrible setback. In the world's worst high-speed train accident to date, catastrophic wheel failure caused a first-generation ICE train to derail at speed at Enschede in Lower Saxony; 101 of the 287 passengers were killed. Following safety improvements, high-speed services now run throughout Germany, as well as on networks into Austria, Switzerland, the Netherlands, Belgium and France.

built in France for a century. This major route accounted for 40 per cent of all rail traffic in France and two main parameters guided the creation of the new line: efficient high-speed operation and environmental impact. The work took four years and used 100,000 tonnes of rails, 1.5 million concrete sleepers and 5.9 million tonnes of ballast for the railbed alone. Almost 400 bridges and tunnels were built along the route, along with underpasses for

animals to cross from one side of the track to the other. To ensure fast running, there are no level crossings on the line, and only gentle curves and gradients. Seven hundred kilometres of high-security fencing prevent any person or animal from getting on the line. The track itself utilises the most up-to-date noise-reduction technology, including long lengths of welded rail, special aggregate for ballast and rubber flanges set between the rails and the sleepers. Opened in 1981, the line enabled TGVs to run at 260km/h from day one, rising to 270km/h in 1983 and 300km/h in 2001. The new Paris–Lyons line almost halved the journey time from three hours 45 minutes to just two hours.

A new rail map of Europe

Spurred on by the success of the TGV, France's Continental neighbours launched their own high-speed railway programmes. In 1988, for example, Italy brought in a high-speed service from Rome to Florence, with ETR 450 trains capable of running at 250km/h. Germany, which had taken a lead with the Munich to Augsburg line in 1965, initially balked at the huge investment needed to create a high-speed network. A strong environmental lobby also opposed what it saw as a blot on the landscape. But in the 1980s new lines gradually took shape, with one linking Hanover and Würzburg and another from Mannheim to Stuttgart. From 1991 sleek new InterCity Express trains

capable of 250km/h began using these lines. In 1992 Spain unveiled a 471km high-speed line from Madrid to Seville, opened to coincide with the Universal Expo held that year in Seville. Spain's AVE trains are French-designed and built, modelled on those running on the TGV Atlantique service, France's second high-speed network, which opened in 1989.

High-speed train (HST) programmes proliferated in the 1990s. In 1994, following the completion of the Channel Tunnel, the Eurostar service was inaugurated offering a three-hour link from London to Paris. Two years later, trains of the Thalys company put Paris just one hour 25 minutes journey time

Undersea journey
Since 1994 Eurostar services have been carrying cars and their passengers through the Channel Tunnel from England to various destinations in Continental Europe. Fire is a very real potential hazard in the tunnel, but so far incidents have been dealt with safely.

Bright new world

The development of high-speed rail services has given rise to some ambitious architectural projects, from the complete refurbishment of London's St Pancras Station, originally built in Victorian times, as a Eurostar terminal to the modernistic steel and glass structure that is Avignon's TGV station (below). On the trains themselves passengers can connect to the Internet (right) and recharge their mobile phones through specially provided sockets. This has helped the service take a share of the lucrative business market from the airlines.

THE BRITISH CONNECTION

For many years after 1994, when the Channel Tunnel opened, Eurostar trains on the London–Paris and London–Brussels services slowed right down on the English end of the journey from the end of the tunnel near Folkestone in Kent to the capital. The lack of a purpose-built high-speed line meant that trains capable of 250–300km/h in northern France had to travel at speeds more suitable for tracks built in Victorian times – trains literally crawled through the dense suburbs of south London to reach the original Eurostar terminus at Waterloo Station. This all changed in 2007 with the completion of the 'High Speed 1' rail link from St Pancras (the new London terminus). Paris is now just two hours 15 minutes away from London.

away from Brussels, three hours 11 minutes from Amsterdam, and three hours 14 minutes from Cologne. These rapid new rail links began to make serious inroads into the air travel market. Unlike at airports, far out on the outskirts of large cities, the new trains brought passengers right into the heart of their destinations. The figures for the TGV train from Paris to Marseilles tell the story: in 2001, 70 per cent of those making this trip chose to fly, but since the inauguration of the TGV service the same proportion of people now take the train. The latest line in France is the TGV Est serving Strasbourg from Paris in two hours 20 minutes, compared to four hours previously, as well as other eastern cities.

Further developments

High-speed rail services have changed people's living and working patterns, with professionals more able and willing to set up home far from their workplace, given the fast connections. It is now easier, for instance, to live in Lille or Tours and commute into Paris than it is to get into the city centre from the suburbs on the local RER network. Despite the inevitable hike in house prices that it brings, cities now clamour to become a stop on a high-speed train route for the economic advantages and growth this brings.

Within a decade, it is projected that regular HST speeds will increase to around 360km/h.

TGV successor
The new AGV train being constructed at La Rochelle in western France. The inclusion of motors under every unit of the train means that longer trainsets can be assembled without compromising speed.

Far Eastern promise
China has a rapidly expanding high-speed rail network with some of the fastest trains in the world today (above). The rolling stock is built in China, but has benefited from collaboration with German (Siemens), Canadian (Bombardier) and French (Alstom) companies.

FAST FREIGHT

Passengers are currently whisked around Europe at speeds of up to 300km/h and soon freight is set to join them. At present, the only freight carried at high speed is mail, but the founding of the Euro Carex project (Euro Cargo Rail Express) in 2009 marked the inception of a plan for a Europe-wide high-speed freight network. The aim is to replace air cargo with train freight over distances of 300 to 800km. The cost of goods carried in this way is estimated at 450 euros a tonne compared to 800 euros average for air freight. Alongside economic advantages, there are clear environmental benefits, with big reductions in carbon emissions. The first stage, due to start in 2012, will link the airports at Roissy, Lyons, Lille, Cologne–Bonn, Amsterdam and Liège with a major terminal east of London on the line from St Pancras to the Channel Tunnel. By 2020 it is envisaged that 22 specially designed freight trains will be able to carry as much cargo around Europe as seven fully-laden Airbus A320 aircraft.

The successor to the French TGV, the AGV (*Automotrice à grande vitesse*), is already in the advanced stages of development. Fifty tonnes lighter than its predecessor, thanks to the use of composite materials, the AGV will also have traction distributed across all its carriages, rather than the current arrangement of separate power cars at each end. Even so, the emphasis is not so much on increasing speed as on using this more flexible train to extend services into Italy, which is set to start in 2011.

On 26 December, 2009, the fastest train line in the world was inaugurated in China. Linking Guangzhou with Wuhan, it carries a brand-new fleet of high-speed trains that can run at an average speed of 350km/h. By 2020 China's railway network will be rebuilt to incorporate eight major high speed routes with a total length of 20,000km. Meanwhile, Argentina is planning a high-speed link of 1,000km from Buenos Aires to Córdoba, which will cut the journey time from 14 hours to just three. This revamped mode of transport is set to go from strength to strength around the world in the coming decades, transforming people's lives.

COMPUTER PRINTERS
Making a better impression

In the 1950s the data produced by the first digital computers was outputted on reams of paper printout. The first devices to be adapted for this task were teleprinters. Advances in printer technology from the 1970s onwards enabled documents to be easily reproduced, not only in the office but increasingly in the home as well.

Printer pandemonium
In a scene from the 1957 romantic comedy His Other Woman, *Katharine Hepburn (on the right) gets into trouble with her boss and the computer's inventor, Spencer Tracy (on the left), for generating four miles of printout.*

Teleprinters were electromechanical typewriters originally conceived as an integral part of Telex networks. In 1954 the Uniprinter, which could print 120 characters per line at 600 lines per minute, was introduced in the United States. Yet the automatic printer market never really took off: in 1963, for example, printer companies specialising in this area sold scarcely more than 50 units a year.

Computer peripherals, which predated actual printers, began to come on the market in the 1970s. One of the first computer printers, the Centronics 101, was unveiled at the National Computer Conference in the USA in 1970. The print head used an innovative seven-wire solenoid impact system, made up of needles moved by electromagnets, making it the first dot-matrix printer in the world. The 'impact' method of printing derived from a long line of typewriter print-head and inked-ribbon technologies, including typebars, golfballs and daisywheels. It is still used today, but its noise restricts it largely to industrial settings.

Inkjet or laser?

In parallel with this, impact-free printing technologies such as laser, inkjet and thermal printing began to be developed. In 1966 the Teletype company launched the Inktronic, the first example of an inkjet printer. Ink held in a small reservoir was sprayed by 40 nozzles onto the sheet of paper in tiny drops that formed the shape of the characters. But the Inktronic proved unreliable and difficult to maintain. The first mass-produced inkjet printer was IBM's 4640, which appeared ten years later. The Japanese manufacturers Canon and Epson followed suit soon after.

Laser technology was pioneered by Xerox in 1971, based on the photocopiers being developed for them by researcher Gary Starkweather. Laser printing utilised the combined effect of light and heat to literally 'bake' the toner – ink in the form of powder in a cartridge – onto the paper. But it was once more IBM who marketed the first laser printer, in 1975.

In 1984 the American company Hewlett-Packard introduced its LaserJet desktop printer, a hugely successful model which by 2009 had sold around 132 million units worldwide.

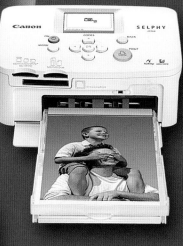

Hewlett-Packard has remained the almost
uncontested market leader in laser printers
(though the print engine inside was developed
by Canon). The following year, Apple entered
the market with its LaserWriter, geared
specially to desktop publishing applications.

Home and office use

Colour printers began to replace black-and-
white in the early 1980s. Manufacturers
competed to produce faster machines that
could offer ever higher print resolution and
ease of use. In general during this period, laser
printers were designed for the professional
market, while printers destined for home use
were customarily inkjets.

As the cost of buying a printer steadily fell,
two diverging trends emerged: at work, people
tended to print out reports and brochures,
while at home, the principal uses were for
correspondence, photographs, business cards
or publicity flyers. Office printing was taking
over tasks that had formerly been the domain
of specialist typesetters and printers, while
personal printing sidelined photo-development
labs and small-scale print shops.

Manufacturers gleaned most of their profits
not from the printers themselves but from
consumables such as cartridges and paper.
Many printers now combine a fax machine, a
photocopier and a scanner, and are cheaper

than ever before. One unsolved problem is the
environmental impact of this remarkable new
technology – in particular how to recycle the
chemicals used in producing toner cartridges.

FIRST OF ITS KIND

The IBM 3800 was the first laser printer
to be produced and sold on a large
scale. It was designed for use by
corporations and companies involved in the
preparation of large volumes of documents
such as bank statements, mailing labels
and invoices. The machine, which was large
and very expensive, could print 20,000 lines
a minute and worked by reflecting laser
beams from an 18-sided mirror spinning at
12,000rpm. Originally launched in 1975,
many IBM 3800s are still in use today.

Photos in a flash
*Attractively
designed, light and
portable colour
printers have
become a key
accessory in the
age of digital
photography.
Printers like the
Canon Selphy
CP-760 (above)
enable people to
print off their own
images at will.*

Rocket ship

The names *Columbia*, *Discovery*, *Challenger*, *Atlantis* and *Endeavour* evoke a new era in space exploration, when NASA abandoned its mighty launch rockets like the Saturn V in favour of reusable spacecraft. Ironically, the shuttle made space flight so commonplace that public interest began to wane, but it was two disasters and escalating costs that would spell the project's end.

On 12 April, 1981, the space shuttle *Columbia* stood ready on launch pad 39A at the Kennedy Space Center in Florida. Attached to the gigantic external fuel tank, filled with a mix of hydrogen and oxygen, the shuttle looked almost fragile. On either side of the tank were huge solid-fuel rocket boosters. The powerful Saturn V rockets that had launched the *Apollo* missions to the Moon were now things of the past. Whereas those mighty rockets and their predecessors had been one-use-only, disposable launch vehicles designed to get their payload into orbit, *Columbia* was the first spacecraft designed to be reusable. Two days after lift-off, when Commander John Young and shuttle pilot Robert Crippen had completed 36 full orbits of the Earth, the shuttle touched down in an aeroplane-style landing on runway 23 at Edwards Air Force Base in California. Space had never seemed so accessible.

A radical new concept

The history of the space shuttle dates back to the triumphant return of the *Apollo 11* astronauts from their Moon landing in July 1969. Flushed with success, NASA began entertaining grandiose dreams of space stations, but then US President Richard Nixon, mired in the war in Vietnam, came to regard space exploration as an expensive luxury the country could ill afford. In March 1970, he informed NASA that they would have to slash the cost of future operations.

The most obvious course would be to design a rocket that could be reused several times. Almost a decade earlier, in 1961, the technicians at NASA's Marshall Space Center had tested the idea of a reusable space vehicle by simulating the splashdown and recovery of a Saturn V rocket motor from the sea. On inspection, the engine was found to be completely intact. From this, they developed the concept of a rocket which, once it had put its payload into orbit, could float down to

Lift-off

The first space shuttle, Columbia, *taking off from Cape Kennedy on 12 April, 1981. In the cockpit were astronauts John Young and Robert Crippen (inset, pictured during a flight simulation session). On this very day, precisely 20 years earlier, the Soviet cosmonaut Yuri Gagarin had made history by becoming the first man in space.*

SPACE ICON

The sleek lines of the space shuttle caught the public's imagination and NASA was quick to seize on the new surge of interest in space flight. The shuttle's elegant delta wing was shaped by the laws of aerodynamics rather than the whims of a designer, and NASA exploited its passing resemblance to a conventional plane to intimate that future space flight would become as straightforward as taking a scheduled flight. The shuttle appeared in a James Bond film of 1979 – *Moonraker* – even before *Columbia* made its maiden flight. Toy manufacturers produced bestselling miniature copies of the shuttle throughout the 1980s. But the *Challenger* disaster of 1986, the spiralling cost of maintenance and delays in making progress gradually brought home that it was not going to be so easy.

Landing like a glider

On 14 April, 1981, Columbia (below) plummeted vertically into the Earth's atmosphere before gliding in to land at Edwards Air Force Base in the Mojave Desert, California.

THE LIFE-SAVING HEATSHIELD

When a space shuttle returns to Earth, it uses the resistance of the planet's atmosphere to slow down its rate of descent. This friction generates temperatures of over 1,600°C, so to protect the craft NASA engineers covered the shuttle in 25,000 heat-resistant ceramic tiles. The tiles are made mostly of silica, from very pure quartz sand, covered with a layer of borosilicate glass. Each tile is slightly different, depending on its position and the heat it must withstand, varying in thickness from 10mm to 100mm. The white tiles on the upper fuselage and wings can resist temperatures of up to 650°C, while the black tiles on the undersurface must withstand 1,200°C. Tiles on the leading edges of the wings, which bear the brunt of re-entry, had to cope with 1,650°C, so were also protected by reinforced carbon-fibre panels.

Vital tilework

Each thermal tile in Columbia's heatshield was individually numbered, and had a precisely allotted space (above). On examination after the maiden flight, 18 of the shuttle's tiles were found to have fallen off, with a further 148 sustaining damage.

Earth on specially designed parachutes. At the same time, other colleagues began investigating the potential for a proper aircraft, somewhat like the experimental X-15 then in service, which was designed to operate in the Earth's stratosphere at an altitude of 100km, where it flew at speeds of up to Mach 6 – six times the speed of sound, or 2,041m/sec.

In 1968 Max Hunter, an engineer at the Lockheed Martin company, brought together these two strands of research in the concept of a module capable of re-entering the Earth's atmosphere to touch down like a plane that would get into space in the first place by piggy-backing on a jettisonable tank used for take-off. In 1971 NASA chief James Fletcher began pleading his case with the Nixon administration, and received the green light in January 1972. The bid to manufacture the space shuttle was won by North American Rockwell aerospace company.

Off the drawing board

The concept of the space shuttle was quite revolutionary. The traditional pattern of a small capsule housing three astronauts in a confined space was replaced by a vehicle that could take seven crew equipped with a hold of 300 cubic metres capable of carrying up to a 25-tonne payload of satellites – far greater than most rockets of the period. The satellites could be placed in orbit by means of a moveable arm. The shuttle was 37 metres in length, with a wingspan of 24 metres, and would descend through the atmosphere at 28,000km/h.

Heat-proof ceramic tiles would protect the craft from burning up during re-entry. But engineers still had to work out how to ensure stability in the descent and safe braking after landing.

The first space shuttle orbiter, *Enterprise*, was rolled out in 1976. With no engines or functional heatshield, this prototype was not designed for space flight, but was intended as a systems test-bed. In 1977 *Enterprise* was

Raw power
The space shuttle Endeavour *lifts off in September 1992. The launch weight of the complete shuttle cluster was 2,000 tonnes, while on landing the orbiter weighed just 100 tonnes. The booster rockets detached just two minutes after launch, followed by the huge fuel tank.*

carried piggy-back on a Boeing 747 to an altitude of 6,700 metres – and released. At the controls was Fred Haise, a veteran of the ill-fated *Apollo 13* mission. After a safe touchdown, parachutes were deployed as brakes on the shuttle. Further test flights were conducted to evaluate the in-flight software. One key consideration was to keep the shuttle steady during re-entry – vital to ensure that the heat-resistant tiles were in their correct positions – as any pilot error might prove fatal.

Construction of *Columbia*, the first shuttle capable of space flight, began in 1975. This craft was subjected to intensive testing from 1979 onwards, before making its historic maiden flight in 1982. Between 1982 and 1985, three more shuttle orbiters joined the fleet: *Challenger*, *Discovery* and *Atlantis*. Shuttles quickly gained a reputation among astronauts for being highly reliable, while their value to the scientific community was to prove incalculable. Scientists from many different disciplines – including physicists, astronomers, biologists and medical researchers – took part

in missions. From 1983 onwards shuttles carried Spacelab, a small laboratory designed to enable scientists to conduct experiments in weightless conditions.

Throughout the early 1980s, the space shuttles enjoyed a stellar career. The images they beamed back enthralled the world, including the Earth viewed from space and astronauts floating free over the cargo dock. The one cloud on the horizon was the escalating cost of the programme; construction alone cost 1 billion dollars – double the original budget. Boosters, engines, special materials and software – everything had to be designed and built from scratch. In addition, months rather than days of inspection were necessary before a relaunch. Repairs were needed after every mission, involving an army of engineers. In matters of maintenance, the shuttle's designers had no precedent to call upon for estimating costs.

Even so, the first 25 shuttle flights were a resounding success. Confidence was high – too high. Pressure to keep up the tight schedule of missions led to the launch of *Challenger* on 28 January, 1986. Just 73 seconds after leaving the launch pad, to the horror of onlookers, the shuttle exploded in the skies above Florida.

Pride of the US nation
Watched by onlookers on the beach near Cape Kennedy (left), Columbia leaves a vapour trail in the skies as she embarks on a mission on 20 June, 1996, to test the effects of gravity on the human body, plants, animals, fluid mechanics and various materials.

Ill-fated flight
The crew of Challenger's *last mission, pictured in November 1985 (below left). Front row, from left to right: Michael J Smith, Francis R 'Dick' Scobee, Ronald E McNair; back row, left to right: Ellison S Onizuka, Christa McAuliffe, Gregory B Jarvis and Judith A Resnick. All seven died when* Challenger *blew up shortly after take-off (below).*

THE *CHALLENGER* DISASTER

On 28 January, 1986, just over a minute after blast-off, the *Challenger* space shuttle broke up, killing all seven crew on board including Christa McAuliffe, a teacher selected from 11,000 applicants to be the first civilian in space. The ensuing congressional enquiry put the blame for the disaster on a combination of cold weather and inadequate maintenance. Just before launch, after a bitterly cold night, smoke was seen coming from one of the 'O'-ring seals joining two stages of the right booster rocket. Under the huge thrust of the launch, a flame leapt through this damaged seal and engulfed the booster, which detached, rupturing the main fuel tank as it did so and causing the massive explosion. The enquiry commission pointed to poor communication between Thiokol, the manufacturers of the boosters who had voiced concerns over the 'O' rings in subzero temperatures, and NASA engineers who had failed to heed the warnings. But final responsibility was laid at the door of the flight directors at Cape Kennedy for allowing the launch to go ahead.

End of an era

The *Challenger* disaster shattered the aura of confidence. All space shuttles were grounded as NASA reviewed its maintenance and safety procedures. By the time flights resumed two and a half years later, the launch schedule was severely compromised. In 1987 construction of *Endeavour* began as a replacement for the lost shuttle. Something of the glory of the early years was recaptured in 1993, when her crew carried out vital repairs to the Hubble Space Telescope. This was a task that could not have been accomplished in any other way.

In the early 1990s, NASA found itself faced with further cuts to its budget. Critics pointed to the

A REMARKABLE FEAT

The Hubble Space Telescope (HST), the world's first such device, was put into low Earth orbit from the cargo bay of the shuttle *Discovery* on 24 April, 1990. Freed from the distortion of the Earth's atmosphere, the telescope would, it was hoped, provide pictures of unparalleled clarity of the cosmos. But Hubble's transmissions turned out to be a blurry disappointment due to flaws in the main mirror. Some minor electrical faults were also detected. In 1993 scientists at the Space Telescope Science Institute in Baltimore put forward a plan to repair the HST by adding what was in effect a correctional lens to alter the focal point and so achieve the intended quality of image. The servicing mission was carried out in December 1993 by the crew of *Endeavour*. Almost 6.5 tonnes of material and some 2,000 tools were required to mount the new lens on the mirror, replace the onboard computer and repair a damaged solar panel. The work involved extremely delicate shifts in the position of the telescope. The operation was a complete success and the HST has since supplied images of astonishing quality. Its operational career will last until 2014.

Space maintenance
NASA astronauts at work in 1993 repairing the flawed mirror and damaged gyroscopes of the Hubble Space Telescope. Since then, four further repair and maintenance missions have been conducted on the HST, the last in May 2009.

Piggy-back ride
The Columbia *space shuttle photographed on the back of a specially adapted Boeing 747 carrier aircraft on 1 March, 2001. The shuttle was being flown from its landing site at Edwards Air Force Base in California to the Kennedy Space Center in Florida, where it would be repaired in readiness for its next mission.*

shuttle's high cost and lack of any clear future role. Then, in the middle of the decade, the USA shelved its plans for a space station to rival the Russian Mir, opting instead for a joint role in the International Space Station (ISS). This immediately gave a new lease of life to the shuttles, which proved ideal platforms for assembling modules for the station in situ. Between 1998 and 2010, they undertook no fewer than 30 missions to this purpose.

In February 2003 disaster struck again. *Columbia*'s heatshield had been damaged during launch, causing the craft to break up as it attempted to re-enter Earth's atmosphere. All seven astronauts on board lost their lives. The accident investigation committee was

Space acrobatics
The shuttle Discovery *(right) rolls onto its back to release the Leonardo cargo module from its cargo bay on 30 August, 2009. The module was designed to transport up to 10 tonnes of freight between Earth and the ISS, where the shuttle was moored for the duration of this mission.*

scathing, highlighting technical shortcomings and accusing NASA of treating the shuttle like an aircraft, rather than the experimental spacecraft that it really was, even after 20 years of service. The myth of a rugged and cheap space freighter was exploded by the disaster.

In January 2004 President George W Bush set new objectives for NASA, which included exploring the solar system via unmanned probes, a return to the Moon and the establishment of bases on Mars. In 2010 the Obama administration cancelled the Moon plans and postponed the manned missions to Mars. Future missions into deep space will require craft more like the old *Apollo* modules, so it came as no surprise when withdrawal of the shuttle from service was announced in September 2010. The last space shuttle flight, of *Atlantis*, blasted off in July 2011.

Collaborative effort
In 1995, in the first operation of its kind, the shuttle Atlantis *docked with the Russian space station* Mir *to resupply it with scientific equipment. Astronauts Bonnie Dunbar and Norman Thagard are seen here inside the Spacelab Science Module.*

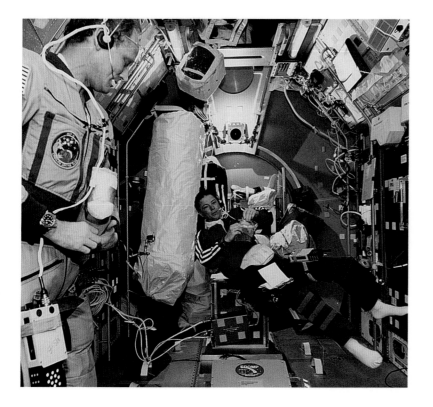

THE ARTISTIC SPIRIT OF INVENTION
Brainwaves and brainstorms

Albert Einstein once claimed that invention was nothing more than offbeat thinking, and some of the surreal, impractical and frankly bizarre devices that people have come up with certainly bear this out. But nowhere is the capacity of the human mind to envisage outlandish artefacts more vividly illustrated than in the work of artists who go far beyond the merely functional.

Curious creation
The Dutch artist Panamarenko pictured at Düsseldorf Art Gallery in 1973 inside the wicker gondola of his 'Aeromodeller', a large PVC dirigible. Panamarenko's elaborate works blend technology and fantasy.

The free play of the human imagination often runs ahead of practicalities, with the result that some inventions have no immediate useful application. For instance, 17 centuries separate James Watt's pioneering 18th-century steam engine from the aeolipile, the world's first theoretical steam turbine described by Hero of Alexandria in the 1st-century AD. Hero's aeolipile worked, but was probably not put to use as an engine – according to some sources, examples were built as toys or curiosities displayed in temples.

Some bright ideas are fated never to get further than the drawing-board. Leonardo da Vinci is probably the best-known exponent of 'nearly-inventions'. He produced drawings of ideas way ahead of their time, but his concepts were flawed: his helicopter could never have flown, his diving suit would have drowned the wearer, his parachute was too heavy to work and his 'tank' was impractical.

As well as drawing-board creations, the history of inventions is littered with examples of devices that remained one-off prototypes that could have become useful artefacts, but for one reason or another failed to make commercial headway. The 'pyréolophore'

A DIFFERENT KIND OF HEATH ROBINSON

The French satirist and science-fiction writer Gaston de Pawlowski (1874–1933, pictured above in a caricature of 1924) delighted in coming up with absurd inventions that undermined the purpose of the original object. His ideas included such brainwaves as the 'safety' boomerang that never returned to the thrower, a bar of 'non-slip' soap studded with nails to stop it slipping through the fingers and a pocket metre-rule just 10cm long. But his side-entry bathtub would eventually become a reality, when it was developed to enable easier access for the elderly and disabled.

developed by the French Niepce brothers in 1807, for example, was an early forerunner of the internal combustion engine that failed to go further. Similarly, Thomas Alva Edison's motion-picture device, the Kinetoscope developed in the 1890s, was a technological dead-end. The Ford Motor Company had plans for nuclear-powered cars in the late 1950s, while Sir Clive Sinclair's C5, an ill-conceived battery-powered electric tricycle, disappeared without trace soon after being launched in a blaze of publicity.

Surreal inventions

During and after the First World War, artists of the Surrealist and Dadaist movements were fascinated by the workings of the subconscious mind. Coupled with their love of playfulness, this led them to embrace the idea of absurd inventions. A leading exponent was Marcel Duchamp (1887–1968), who was influenced by the satirist Gaston de Pawlowski and dreamed up gadgets with purely 'symbolic' functions, such as as his 'bachelor machine'.

In Britain at around the same time, the illustrator William Heath Robinson (1872–1944) began producing a series of drawings of eccentric machines that he called 'Absurdities'. These wonderfully inventive contraptions performed simple tasks in crazily complicated ways that could never have worked in reality, and 'Heath-Robinson' entered the language as a byword for impossibly complex technology. In the 1930s his humorous drawings – which included 'Testing Corn Plasters in the Salon of a Fashionable West End Chiropodist', 'The Professor's Invention for Peeling Potatoes' and 'A Little Mechanical Help in Rising Gracefully from a Lounge Chair' – earned him the nickname 'The Gadget King'.

Art and technology

The dividing line between technological inventiveness and artistic creativity can be a

Objet d'art
With flywheels and runners made from recycled iron, Jean Tinguely's Bascule VI ('Rocker No.6') suggests a utilitarian purpose but in fact it has no practical function whatever and is an exhibit at Nantes Art Museum.

fine one. The artist Panamarenko (real name Henri van Herwegen) used his professional training as an engineer specialising in fluid mechanics to create eccentric 'flying' machines like his 'Scotch Gambit', a massive hovercraft with the appearance of an insect, which he constructed from three and a half tonnes of metal parts. Panamarenko's abstract dirigibles, flying saucers and other (non-)flying machines recall Leonardo's sketches, or some of the genuine but improbable contraptions devised by early flying enthusiasts trying to get off the ground. These ranged from the *Passarola*, a wind and magnet-propelled airship with a boat-shaped body and birdlike wings and head, invented by the Brazilian priest Bartolomeu de Gusmão in 1709, to the pedal-driven machine (1885) of American inventor Dr William Orville Ayres, which resembled nothing so much as a flying bedstead. (The nickname 'Flying Bedstead' would later be given to the experimental vertical take-off rig built by Rolls-Royce and first tested in 1954.)

The avant-garde Swiss artist Jean Tinguely (1925–91) was neither a mechanic nor an engineer, but nevertheless created sculptural machines in the Dadaist tradition. The generic term he applied to his assemblages made from reclaimed materials was 'metamechanics', while individual pieces were given titles such as *Rotozazas* and *Heureka*. Tinguely also built

Caught up in free thought
The American artist Alexander Calder in a portrait taken in 1929 by the celebrated Hungarian photographer André Kertész (left). Three years earlier, Calder had created his famous 'Cirque', a miniature circus made from wire, string, rubber bands and other found materials.

'Unfindable objects'
Two drawings by Jacques Carelman. Below: a coffee pot for a masochist, which the artist captioned 'We believe that the drawing is sufficiently self-explanatory that we need not dwell on the details, which could be painful'. And right: the 'swing designed for a flat'.

machines that self-destructed after half an hour. The American painter and sculptor Alexander Calder (1898–1976), who was a qualified engineer, made sculptures comprising independently moving elements driven by an electric motor or a hand crank. In a society where we are surrounded by machines, artists like these have deconstructed the technology-obsessed world by building useless machines with a purely playful purpose.

Impossible constructions

Jacques Carelman, a painter, theatre designer and illustrator born in France in 1929, is known for the creation of what he called 'Unfindable Objects' – everyday household items tweaked to subvert their function. His *Catalogue* of 1969 immediately tickled the public's fancy with his drawings of items such

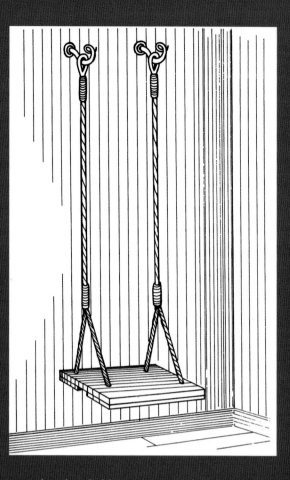

THE WEIRD WORLD OF GLEN BAXTER

The British cartoonist Glen Baxter is an acknowledged master of the surreal and absurd. Born in 1944 in Leeds, he blends elements of pulp fiction, popular children's comics and adventure books of the 1920s–50s into his drawings, liberally laced with highbrow literary and artistic references. His cartoons have appeared in publications as august and diverse as *The New Yorker, Vanity Fair* and *Le Monde*. Baxter peoples his drawings with colonial adventurers, schoolboys in blazers, cowboys and gangsters, placed in the most unlikely and fantastic situations. The cartoons are accompanied by deliberately laconic, ill-matched or absurd captions. Baxter drew his inspiration from absurdist precursors such as Lewis Carroll, Alfred Jarry (the French creator of Père Ubu), Man Ray, Samuel Beckett and René Magritte. The gadgets and inventions in his art invariably fail: a prehistoric stone yo-yo threatens to crush its creator, while the world's first pencil sharpener (below) looked more like a turbine generator.

as a glass-headed hammer, a pocket doormat and a deck of transparent playing cards. Some of Carelman's inventions owe much to the work of earlier artists who played around with optical illusions and geometrical puzzles. The Swede Oscar Reutersvärd (1915–2002), for example, who was known as the 'father of the impossible figure' and the English artist William Hogarth (1697–1764), whose engraving *Satire on False Perspective* of 1754 shows a man in the foreground fishing in a river that appears to be in the far distance, among other absurdities.

The most famous of all these 'artists of the impossible' was the Dutch draughtsman M C Escher (1898–1972) who exploited mathematical phenomena such as the Möbius strip, the endless staircase and tessellations to create an intricately imagined topsy-turvy world of impossible constructions. One of his most celebrated lithographs is *Relativity* (1953), which shows a person ascending a staircase from multiple perspectives simultaneously, leaving the viewer with a dizzying, kaleidoscopic impression. The Swiss artist Markus Raetz, born in 1941, has also made the phenomenon of perception the subject of his work. His manipulation of the visual world through metamorphoses and distortions subverts our conventional ways of seeing and making sense of the world.

Fictional inventions

Some of the most memorable and fantastic inventions have been spawned by writers and film-makers. In 1726, in the satirical work *Gulliver's Travels*, the Irish writer Jonathan Swift conceived of a flying island called Laputa, where science is misapplied to the creation of ridiculous inventions, such as the 'text breeding machine'. This mechanical device generates

Impossible triangle
A sculpture by French magician Francis Tabary, created in honour of Lionel Penrose.

THE PENROSE STAIRS

The British psychiatrist, geneticist and mathematician Lionel Penrose first published his concept of the impossible Penrose Stairs or Penrose Steps (shown below) in the February 1958 issue of the *British Journal of Psychology*. The drawing depicts an impossible continuous staircase, featuring four 90-degree turns, that eternally ascends (or descends). On Penrose's impossible staircase a person could walk on endlessly, yet never get any higher or lower. The two-dimensional drawing achieves this paradox by distorting perspective, but in the real, three-dimensional world such a construction would clearly be impossible. Escher used the Penrose stair concept in two of his most famous lithographs, *Ascending and Descending* (1960) and *Waterfall* (1961).

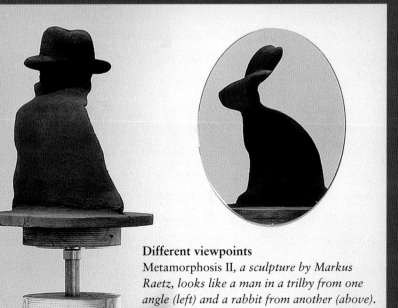

Different viewpoints
Metamorphosis II, *a sculpture by Markus Raetz, looks like a man in a trilby from one angle (left) and a rabbit from another (above).*

THE TIME MACHINE

The brainchild of H G Wells, novelist and master of science fantasy, the Time Machine was a futuristic invention that enabled the anonymous hero (Wells named him simply the 'Time Traveller') to explore the fourth dimension. The device propels the traveller forward in time to AD 802,701, where he encounters a terrifying vision of the future: a world controlled by a terrible ape-like race, the Morlocks, which turns into a wasteland inhabited by crabs. After a brief return to his contemporary world, curiosity gets the better of the Time Traveller and he vanishes again – this time without a trace.

Bumpy ride
Actor Rod Taylor at the controls of the Time Machine in the 1960 screen adaptation of H G Wells's Victorian fantasy novel. In a homage to the original author, the artistic director of MGM studios mounted a brass plaque on the machine bearing the legend 'Manufactured by H George Wells'.

Awesome sound
Cartoon character Gaston Lagaffe (below) playing his fearsome instrument, the Gaffophone, which made its first appearance in the comic-book Spirou *on 9 March, 1967.*

arbitrary combinations of letters, with which 'the most ignorant Person may write Books in Philosophy, Poetry, Politicks, Law, Mathematicks and Theology, without the Least Assistance from Genius or Study'. Mary Shelley, in her 1818 novel *Frankenstein*, described a machine that the eponymous central character uses to create human life, albeit in a grotesquely debased form. And most famously, H G Wells introduced the concept of time travel in his

work of 1895, *The Time Machine*. The Time Machine was brought to cinema screens in 1960, but it has often been the villains who constructed the fiendish devices in films, as in those based on writer Ian Fleming's famous spy character James Bond. *Dr No* (1962) featured a flame-throwing armoured car, while Largo, the criminal mastermind in *Thunderball* (1965), built a submersible laboratory. A more benign fantastic invention was the vintage car

THE MIGHTY GAFFOPHONE

The imaginary instrument called the 'Gaffophone' (or 'Flaterfoon' in Flemish) was dreamt up in the late 1960s by Belgian cartoonist Franquin. His character Gaston Lagaffe/Guust Flater is a truly inept musician who builds his monstrous instrument from a hollowed-out tree trunk, with wires attached as strings. The Gaffophone emits a horrible sound that invariably results in massive destruction. It was supposedly inspired by an African harp that the illustrator saw at the Belgian Royal Museum for Central Africa at Tervuren on the outskirts of Brussels.

the user, and are generally worse than useless. These include spectacles with built-in fans to stop you from crying when slicing onions, the all-day tissue dispenser (a toilet roll fixed on top of a hat) for hay-fever sufferers and duster-slippers for cats so they can help with the housework.

Two British inventors of useless objects who have taken eccentric gadgetry to new heights are Rowland Emmett (1906–90) and Tim Hunkin, who was born in 1950. As seems to be a common trend, both were originally cartoonists. Emmett, who built the car for *Chitty Chitty Bang Bang*, made kinetic sculptures that functioned perfectly to no purpose, such as his water-powered musical clock, 'The Aqua Horological Tintinnabulator'. Hunkin, who for many years drew a popular science cartoon strip entitled 'The Rudiments of Wisdom' for the *Observer* , has constructed such whimsical devices as the 'Autofrisk' in which a series of inflated rubber gloves pat the user down, as in a security search, and the 'Expressive Photobooth', where hidden mechanisms like gusts of air and bright lights cause the user to pull odd expressions just as the pictures are taken.

Domestic harmony
French inventor Marcel Betrisey's came up with this 'middle-of-the-bed indicator' (left), designed to settle marital disputes over bed space. It is made out of part of an old sewing machine for the base, a pétanque ball and a small laser torch mounted on a bendy metal strip.

THE LANDFILL PRIZE

Consumerism has given rise to many truly useless gadgets. In 2008, to 'celebrate the stupendous creativity of the people tasked with inventing constantly inflated new wants for us to want', British ecological activist John Naish inaugurated the annual Landfill Prize for the most pointless consumer product. Nominations have included a battery-powered hot-air ear dryer, a fishing chair with built-in loudspeakers and the 'Uroclub', a hollow plastic golf club into which a (male) golfer can urinate if caught short during a round.

that could fly in the 1968 *Chitty Chitty Bang Bang*, a film loosely based on a children's book that was also written by Ian Fleming. Remarkable cars are a perennial favourite of film-makers: in 1985 director Robert Zemeckis updated H G Wells's time travel concept in *Back to the Future*. An eccentric inventor modifies a DeLorean DMC-12, a gullwing-doored sports car that was a spectacular 'white elephant' in real life, into a time machine that transports the film's hero back to 1955.

Useless inventions

Some fantastical inventions have a deliberately satirical purpose, being designed to lampoon the consumer society's obsession with constant innovation and excess. This is the driving force behind the inventions of Kenji Kawakami, master of the Japanese art of *Chindogu* (literally, 'unusual tool'). Kawakami and his followers devise ingenious gadgets apparently designed to solve a particular problem, but which turn out to generate new problems of their own, or bring social embarrassment to

Housework made easy
Slippers built into a dustpan and brush (above) – one of the ingenious ideas in Jacques Carelman's 'Catalogue of Unfindable Objects'.

Gadget guru
Kenji Kawakami in 2006 (right), wearing an umbrella tie and a pair of eye-dropper glasses, just two of his numerous 'Un-useless Inventions'.

Revealing the minutest detail

Exceptional detail
A molecule of phtalocyanine as seen under a scanning tunnelling microscope. This metallo-organic material is used, among other applications, to make green and blue pigments for the dyestuff industry.

In March 1981, Gerd Binnig and Heinrich Rohrer, two physicists working at the IBM research centre in Zurich, Switzerland, made a discovery that would revolutionise the world of imaging. The tunnel-effect microscope that they invented enabled researchers to study the composition of matter at the atomic level. The technology proved tailor-made for the development and manufacture of nano-materials.

Imaging breakthrough
Swiss physicist Heinrich Rohrer (left, on the left) and German physicist Gerd Binnig (on the right) adjusting a sample in the chamber of their scanning tunnelling microscope (STM) at IBM's Research Laboratory in Zurich.

JUST REWARD

Binnig and Rohrer were awarded the 1986 Nobel prize for physics for their breakthrough invention of the scanning tunnelling microscope. The prize was shared with Ernst Rushka, an older German physicist who designed the first electron microscope.

Gerd Binnig and Heinrich Rohrer were both specialists in quantum physics working on a phenomenon that was only observable on an infinitely microscopic scale: the tunnel effect. Their experiment drew on research done in the 1970s by the American physicist Russell Young. It consisted of bringing the tip of a needle sharpened to a point no wider than a nanometre (one millionth of a millimetre) to within a few atomic diameters of a metal specimen, or a semiconductor. When voltage was applied across the two objects, the needle drew electrons away from the piece of metal, thus generating a measurable electric current. The scientists later found that the strength of this current varied according to the distance of the stylus from the metal surface.

Atoms at the end of the tunnel

Binnig and Rohrer used this discovery to develop a completely new kind of microscope, which they unveiled in 1983. Unlike optical or traditional electron microscopes, which beam rays of light or bundles of electrons at the object under scrutiny, their instrument used the sharpened metal stylus like a scanner. When the needle moved over the surface of the study sample, a device – consisting of three piezoelectric ceramics that dilated or contracted – adjusted the height of the stylus by infinitesimal degrees in order to sustain a constant electric current.

These tiny movements were logged by a computer and in this way the scientists managed to image a specimen of silicon in such fine detail that it was possible to make out individual metallic atoms, each of which was around one ångström (one tenth of a nanometre) wide. Thus, while the scanning electron microscope (SEM) was capable of magnifications between 100,000 and 2 million times, the new scanning tunnelling microscope (STM) could achieve magnifications of up to 100 million. This made it possible to scan the surface of materials and produce an image of them at the atomic level. For the first time, it gave physicists the opportunity to observe with their own eyes quantum effects that had once been confined to the realms of the theoretical.

The atomic microscope

The STM paved the way for further instruments exploiting the interaction between atoms. In 1986 Binnig, along with Swiss physicist Christoph Gerber and American Calvin Quate, developed the atomic force microscope (AFM). On this, a stylus made of diamond, tungsten or silicon is lowered directly onto the surface to be investigated; a constant infinitesimal difference is maintained between the sample surface and the tip by the phenomenon known as Van der Waals' forces (the sum of the forces of attraction

Ultrasensitive
Scanning tunnelling microscopes are so highly sensitive they are fitted with a damper to absorb the vibrations caused by the researcher's voice or by colleagues moving around the laboratory.

and repulsion between molecules). The tip is mounted on an extremely sensitive lever and its tiny movements are monitored by laser. The advantage of this process is that it can be used on non-conducting materials such as ceramics, polymers or even organic matter. The AFM has enabled scientists to scrutinise the living world as never before, making it possible to study DNA and the interactions between living proteins in undreamt-of detail. It has made a major contribution to gene therapy.

Manipulating atoms

STMs can not only identify individual atoms, but can also be used to manipulate them. The tip is so fine they can lift or depress single atoms. In 1989 IBM researcher Donald Eigler used the technique to write the IBM acronym on 35 individual atoms of xenon on a nickel base. He proved that the STM was capable of atomic-scale precision, paving the way for the construction of infinitely small structures. Rather than having to miniaturise components by paring down or shaping material, engineers can now build structures from first principles on a nanometric scale by assembling atoms like Lego bricks. The STM truly opened the door to the thrilling new world of nanotechnology.

A FINE POINT OF DISTINCTION

The highest quality scanning tunnelling micrographs are obtained from instruments fitted with a stylus honed to the finest possible point – ideally to the width of a single atom. To produce a stylus of this quality a thread of silver or tungsten wire one-quarter of a millimetre in diameter is immersed in a corrosive solution of chemicals that eat away the tip until the desired thickness is reached. An alternative method of manufacture is to stretch a gold filament to breaking point.

Finely tuned adjustments
The sample is positioned on the microscope with fine tweezers, then the stylus is moved into place by a servo motor that shifts in increments of a single micron. The inset (right) shows a false-colour scanning tunnelling micrograph of DNA. The image is formed by scanning a fine point just above the specimen surface and electronically recording the height of the point as it moves.

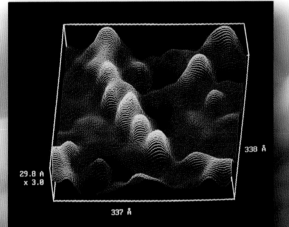

338 Å

29.8 Å
x 3.0

337 Å

Airbags 1981

The airbag car safety device was first introduced on a large scale by Mercedes-Benz in 1981. It is an inflatable bag built into a car's steering column or dashboard that fills instantly with compressed air or gas if the vehicle is in a frontal collision. It protects the head and chest of the driver or passenger from serious injury. The invention goes back to 1952, when a retired American engineer named John W Herrick first came up with the idea for such a safety device. In 1964 the US company of Eaton, Yale and Towne developed a prototype and the very first airbags appeared in American automobiles from 1973 onwards.

Mercedes-Benz, who had begun to take an interest in the American work in 1969, launched its own version of the airbag in the late 1970s. In 1980 the German firm first began fitting airbags to all its top-of-the-range models. In the case of an impact, their system locked the seatbelt and deployed the airbag within 100 to 150 milliseconds. In 1994 the Swedish carmaker Volvo introduced side-impact airbags. It is estimated that wearing a seatbelt and having an airbag fitted reduces the chance of being killed in a collision by 68 per cent, and some 55 million vehicles in Europe are now equipped with them.

Lifesaving sack
Steering-column airbags for drivers were the first to appear, followed by front-passenger airbags, side-impact airbags, airbags to protect the knees and finally curtain airbags to shield car occupants from flying glass. Waistcoat-like airbags became available for motorbike riders in 2008.

Transdermal patches 1981

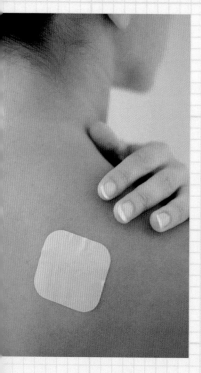

Approved for use by the US Food and Drug Administration in December 1979 and going on general sale from 1981, the first self-adhesive transdermal delivery system (TDDS) patch was designed to deliver a dose of scopolamine against travel sickness. By infusing a drug into the blood through the skin, the method avoided side effects that can arise from taking a medication orally, such as irritation of the digestive tract or degradation of the active ingredient in the intestine.

Today, patches are most commonly associated with people trying to quit smoking by taking controlled-release doses of nicotine, but they are also used to diffuse drugs to treat a whole variety of other conditions, such as angina and certain symptoms of Alzheimer's Disease, as well as hormonal treatments (such as contraceptive patches) and analgesics to alleviate pain. Yet the skin is a very effective barrier and not all medications have molecules small enough to pass through it.

NICOTINE PATCHES

In 1990 Murray Jarvik, Professor of Psychiatry and Pharmacology at the University of California in Los Angeles, with his colleague Jed Rose devised a transdermal system for diffusing nicotine directly into the bloodstream to help smokers resist cravings for a cigarette. Nicotine patches became available on prescription in the United States from 1992, and became available over the counter four years later in both the USA and Europe. Despite the fact that they do nothing to reduce nicotine dependence, nicotine patches double a person's chances of quitting smoking within six months to a year.

Easy birth control
The contraceptive patch (left), introduced in 2001, administers a steady dose of oestrogen and progesterone over a week.

Oncogenics 1982

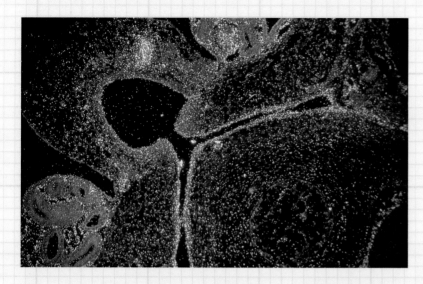

these genes play an active part in mechanisms controlling cell multiplication. Their alteration explained the phenomenon of unbridled cell growth, a key characteristic of cancers. This discovery opened up a whole new field of research. During the 1980s, a series of new oncogenes were identified. Research into the role they play in the growth of cancers has brought crucial advances in the development of new diagnostic tools and treatments.

Pointing towards trouble
The arrow-headed formation in this cross-section of a chicken embryo indicates RNA anomalies that will lead to the formation of oncogenes in the internal tissues of the creature's blood vessels.

In the 1970s there were two competing theories to explain the origin of cancers. Some researchers pointed to a viral source on the basis that certain viruses were known to induce cancers in organisms they infected. Others suggested that cancers were more likely to have a genetic root, given that agents which were known to be carcinogenic, such as sunlight, X-rays, tobacco and various chemical compounds, had mutagenic effects – that is, they altered cell DNA.

Since then, developments in genetic engineering have shown that the two theories were by no means irreconcilable. In 1976 Harold Varmus, Michael Bishop and Dominique Stehelin of the University of California succeeded in isolating and identifying a cancer-causing gene within the Rous Sarcoma virus that caused solid tumour growth in chickens. Then, in 1982, three separate American research teams led respectively by Robert Weinberg, Geoffrey Cooper and Michael Wigler, isolated a gene associated with human bladder cancers that could induce malignant tumour growth in cells cultivated in vitro.

Altered genes

Study of these cancer-inducing genes (named oncogenes from the Greek *oncos*, meaning 'tumour'), whether derived from viruses or cancerous cells, indicated that they were a slightly altered form of genes normally found in perfectly healthy cells. Another major finding to come from the research was that

Cancer growth
In this artist's impression of a white blood cell or lymphocyte (below), the double helix of the chromosome, two strands of DNA, are in an abnormal position. This anomaly prompts production of fusion (or chimeric) proteins (shown in green). This in turn generates a unique code of gene sequences that enables this abnormal, cancerous cell to evade its pre-programmed death and multiply.

A COMPLEX DISEASE

Several factors come into play in the appearance of a cancer. Some people present a greater risk of contracting cancer as a result of hereditary flaws in their genetic make-up. But the appearance of a cancer also depends to a great extent either upon lifestyle choices (for instance, excessive tanning without using sun-block, smoking or excessive alcohol consumption) or on infection by certain viruses, such as the papilloma virus and hepatitis B.

Home movies made easy

In 1982 two Japanese companies, Sony and JVC, announced that the videotape recorder and a camera would soon be combined in a single device. The gadget that video professionals had been waiting for was about to be unveiled. Light and versatile, the camcorder soon gained a huge market among consumers at large.

Close-up
The Kodak Zoom 8, launched in the early 1960s, was one of the first ciné cameras to allow the amateur film-maker to zoom in on a subject without having to stop filming.

system that could transmit video footage as soon as filming was over was the 'Portapak' introduced by Sony in 1967. It was marketed as portable, but the apparatus weighed 15 kilos, so even though it was supposedly designed for use by a single operator, in practice it took a two-person team to use it on location. The Portapak kit consisted of a black-and-white camera linked by cable to a

Moving pictures
Tourists armed with cameras and video cameras stand ready outside the gates of Buckingham Palace to take shots of the Queen and royal family in the summer of 1971.

The history of the camcorder is closely linked to that of the small screen, as TV journalists and cameramen sought to provide viewers with on-the-spot live images from trouble spots and other newsworthy events. Up until the late 1960s, filming an outside broadcast meant transporting a lorry-load of equipment and a small army of technicians to the location. At the time TV cameras used electronic tubes to convert light into electrical impulses and these tubes would heat up during filming, twisting and distorting the image, so the operator constantly had to recalibrate the equipment.

Super 8 and the Portapak

In 1965 Kodak launched its Super 8 movie film. The cameras marketed to use this film format – which with their pistol grips looked almost like portable drills – could capture three minutes of continuous filming at 18 frames per second on one spool of film. By 1974 the Super 8 technology was also able to record sound. But the film itself still had to be developed in the same laborious way as still photographs. The first independent recording

THE PORTAPAK REVOLUTION

Video professionals working for television networks or as freelancers took a keen interest in the Portapak system. Campaigning groups saw it as a powerful new tool for recording instances of state brutality against Civil Rights protesters and anti-Vietnam war activists in the late 1960s. The amateur documentaries they made presented a take on contemporary life that contrasted with the sanitised version being shown by TV networks. The police used the same technology for surveillance of demonstrators. Companies used Portapak to promote their public image, or in corporate videos tutoring their sales force in marketing techniques. It was put to similar use by athletes to hone their performance.

Trailblazer
The first mass-market camcorder was the Sony Betamovie BMC–100P, launched in 1983.

record-only VCR tape unit that was the size of a small suitcase. Despite being somewhat unwieldy to use, it revolutionised outside broadcasting and was standard equipment for news reports and documentaries for the next 15 years. At £1,000 it was expensive, but just about affordable for keen home-movie buffs.

Colour was introduced in professional film recording equipment from the early 1970s onwards. Yet it was 1982 before Sony and JVC finally managed to combine the VCR unit and the camera within the same device: the camcorder.

War of the video formats

The rival Japanese companies soon found themselves in a bitter struggle over whose system would capture the market. In 1983 Sony made the first move when it launched its Betamovie BMC–100P, the first mass-market camcorder. This shoulder-mounted camera recorded footage on half-inch Betamax videotape cassettes, which had been introduced in 1975 and were based on an old professional format. Sony's camcorder weighed just 2.5kg and could record for more than three hours on a single cassette, with sound recorded through an inbuilt microphone. In addition, it had a 6X magnification zoom function.

In 1976 Kodak announced the KodaVision 2000 camcorder manufactured by Matsushita. Unlike the Sony model, it had autofocus and used smaller 8-mm cassettes. That same year

Quality control
Testing the image quality of a new camcorder by means of a test card placed 1.5m from the camera. The card is filmed, then its image is projected onto a screen for comparison with the original.

JVC introduced its GR-C1 camcorder. Not only did this use JVC's own Compact VHS tape, one-third the size of other cassettes, it could also play back directly through a TV without having to remove the cassette and put it in a videotape player. This prompted Sony to abandon the Betamovie and introduce a camcorder capable of recording video on standard 8-mm tape. Soon a whole host of other manufacturers joined the fray, including General Electric, Philips, Polaroid and Fujifilm.

The camcorder was an instant hit with consumers: in 1985 alone, almost half a million were sold worldwide. Three years later, the annual figure had reached 3 million. Sales were dominated by the Japanese firms Sony, JVC and Panasonic. Competition now focused on picture quality. In 1989 JVC launched S-VHS, a new format that offered better image definition and colour resolution through the use of 420 lines per picture height (as against 240 lines on standard VHS). Sony responded with Hi8, an improved version of its

Memory bank
Camcorders have become a popular way for people to capture holiday memories. There are special antishock and waterproof models aimed at the extreme sports enthusiast.

HOW A CAMCORDER WORKS

The lens of a camcorder focuses the light on an electronic sensor. Hundreds of tiny diodes measure the light striking them and generate a small electric current. Each of these diodes is composed of millions of light-sensitive cells that detect red, green and blue wavelengths. Some high-end camcorders have a sensor that can pick up the whole spectrum of individual colours. The video signal transmitted is recorded either onto magnetic tape (on analogue models) or sent to a signal converter that encodes the information as binary data (on digital models).

Video. But little by little, VHS captured the lion's share of the consumer camcorder market, while Betamax became the industry standard for professional video recording.

Age of the amateur cameraman

As the retail price of camcorders continued to fall, the market saw double-digit growth year-on-year. While most amateur footage showed scenes of everyday family life or holiday adventures, the boom in the ownership of camcorders increased the likelihood of an amateur film-maker being in the right place at the right time when a major news event occurred. Television networks no longer had a monopoly on capturing moving images of incidents like riots, natural disasters or wars.

Some pieces of amateur footage were aired nationwide or even globally: the unprovoked assault on black motorist Rodney King by

Los Angeles police officers in 1991, which sparked rioting and an enquiry into racism and police brutality in the USA, came to light through a VHS recording made by a witness. On a lighter note, the camcorder boom gave rise to humorous home-video TV shows like *You've Been Framed*.

Camcorders became even easier to use in 1992 when Sharp unveiled the world's first camcorder with a 4-inch colour LCD monitor in place of the traditional viewfinder. Able to swivel and tilt, this allowed users to select better shots by viewing the subject from different angles, and to instantly review what they had just filmed.

Enter the digital camcorder

The appearance of the digital camcorder in 1995 – the first ones on the market were made by Sony and Panasonic, with JVC and Sharp hard on their heels – put an end to the video format wars. Resolution of 500 lines now became the norm. As a result of the introduction of MiniDV (Digital Video) cassettes the following year, camcorders were produced that could be held in the palm of the hand. The first model capable of recording straight onto DVD was manufactured by Hitachi in 2000.

High-definition images were the next innovation, in 2003, followed in 2004 by camcorders with a hard disk and flash memory. But latterly camcorders have found their market squeezed by the growing sophistication of digital cameras, which can now take video footage, as well as by mobile phones with the same function.

VIDEO EDITING FOR ALL

Prior to the late 1980s, editing video footage meant running the selected film sequences through a scanner and recording them onto a VCR unit. But with the advent of digital video, camcorders now come equipped with FireWire ports that link them directly to computers. Dedicated software applications allow users to edit the video footage in whatever way they wish, and to add effects that were once the sole preserve of professionals, such as fade-outs and fade-ins, intercutting or background music. Editing has recently become even easier through the appearance of camcorders with hard drives or flash memory that can transfer videos instantly to the computer screen in the form of digital files; all that is needed is a USB connection.

Light and portable
Sony's 'Handycam' weighs just 230 grams (without batteries or cassette). The AVCHD format enabled camcorders to be miniaturised without compromising picture quality. Users can now film for hours without having to change the flash memory card.

The bee man

As a result of his ingenious experiments, the Austrian zoologist and ethologist Karl von Frisch uncovered many surprising and hitherto unsuspected aspects of animal behaviour. His most famous discovery revealed how bees communicate with one another about food sources. Bees, it seemed, were far more intelligent than anyone had thought.

On 10 December, 1973, at the age of 87, the Austrian scholar Karl von Frisch was awarded the Nobel prize in physiology and medicine by the King of Sweden. This supreme honour was in recognition of a career spent observing animals. 'Even before I went to school', Frisch wrote in his autobiography in 1957, 'I had a little zoo in my room.' His childhood collection comprised a hundred different creatures, including birds, amphibians and fish. This precocious interest in the natural world came from the long walks he used to take in the Viennese countryside, but also from a solid scientific background in his upbringing. Karl's father was a doctor, his mother came from a long line of distinguished scholars and scientists, and it was in the company of his uncle Sigmund Exner, a physiologist, that he undertook his earliest studies into animal behaviour in the late 1900s. But his personal

Social animals
A computer illustration of the honey bee 'waggle dance' by which a bee indicates the location of food to other bees. When a foraging bee finds food, it returns to the hive and performs a figure-of-eight. The orientation of the central line of the dance points to the food source in relation to the Sun.

Close study
Karl von Frisch studying bees in his garden in 1964.

preference was not really for the kind of animal research that involved dissecting crabs or implanting electrodes into frogs.

The colourful world of animals

After initially enrolling as a medical student in Vienna, von Frisch soon transferred to the Zoological Institute of the University of Munich in 1910 to focus on ethology, or animal behaviour. His first subject of study was of light and colour perception in minnows. To do this, he first habituated the fish to a piece of blue cardboard behind their feeder in the aquarium. When he switched this to a red card, the minnows stopped feeding as they associated food with the colour blue, proving that the fish could perceive colour.

Poor eyesight rendered von Frisch exempt from conscription in the First World War, but he volunteered to work at a Red Cross hospital in Bavaria, where he set up a bacteriological laboratory. It was there that he began his famous studies on bees in his leisure hours. By setting out dishes of sugared water for scout bees and observing their behaviour, he determined that they, too, had colour perception. This controversial finding flew in the face of the orthodox view of the time, which refused to accept that such lowly creatures as bees could share a complex physiological function with humans.

The bee dance

It was in the spring of 1919 that von Frisch made what he called 'the most far-reaching observation of my life' He noticed that scout bees, after feeding from one of the sugar-water dishes, would return to the hive and perform a frenetic 'dance' in front of other forager bees from the colony, which then quite literally made a beeline for the food source. Appointed director of the Zoologic Institute at Rostock University in 1921, he proceeded to study this remarkable behaviour over the next 20 years.

Using a special transparent hive, von Frisch gradually gained further insights into the 'language' of bees when communicating the location of a food source. If the source was nearby, the bee performed a circular dance: in this case, most information is conveyed by the smell of the pollen on the bee's back. But if the source was far-off, the bee performed what is known as the 'waggle dance', indicating the position of the food in relation to the Sun. Distance from the source was shown by the speed of the bee's gyrations. Von Frisch surmised that the bees' perfectly calibrated internal 'clock', which took into account the movement of the Sun in the sky, gave them the capacity to find their way back to a source of food that they had left some hours previously. This was corroborated by their ability, after swarming, to construct the internal layout of a new hive on exactly the same axis as the mother hive.

Throughout his long and eminent career, von Frisch never lost his youthful sense of wonderment at the profundity of animal intelligence. He concluded that 'every single species of the animal kingdom challenges us with all, or nearly all, the mysteries of life'.

WARNING SIGNALS

Researcher James Nieh of the University of California at San Diego has shown that bees are capable of warning other bees of impending danger. They do this by nodding the head and emitting faint beeping sounds.

Radar-tracked bee

As part of pollination research, a scientist at the National Resources Institute at Malvern in Worcestershire uses a projected image produced by a harmonic radar system to track the flight path of a tagged bumble bee. Tagged bees appear as 'blips' on the radar screen. The tags have an antenna that reflects a component (harmonic) of the incoming radar waves. By looking for harmonic reflections, extraneous 'noise' from obstacles like vegetation is eliminated.

FRACTALS – 1982
Hidden patterns

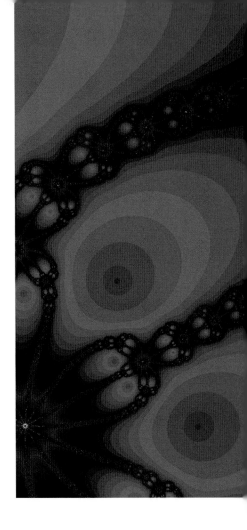

While studying financial market trends in the 1960s, the French-American mathematician and economist Benoît Mandelbrot noticed that a trading chart for a day of activity looked just like the chart for a week, or a month, or a decade. This led him to study recurring patterns that remain the same even though the scale of time – or space – changes. He expounded his revolutionary ideas on these 'fractals', as he called them, in his seminal work published in 1982, *The Fractal Geometry of Nature*.

Patterns in the sand
The amazing dune patterns of the Grand Erg Occidental in Algeria (left), in a photograph taken by the French aerial photographer Yann Arthus-Bertrand. With no marker of scale, it is impossible to tell whether the image was taken from the height of a person or from an overhead plane.

Mandelbrot first coined the term 'fractal' (from the Latin *fractus*, meaning 'broken' or 'fractured') in 1975, defining it as 'a rough or fragmented geometric shape that can be split into parts, each of which is a reduced-size copy of the whole'. It was this 'self-similarity', the distinctive feature of fractals, that made them the subject of such intense fascination for the mathematician. The property manifested itself, for example, in graphs tracing the movement of particles in suspension in a liquid (Brownian motion): the paths they take always have the same factional dimension, irrespective of whether one views them in microcosm or on

Natural order
The Romanesco broccoli, seen in close-up (left), is one of the most famous examples of complex recurring fractal patterns in nature. Other instances include snow or ice crystals and the leaves of ferns.

TAMING MONSTERS

In the early 20th century, some mathematicians who looked beyond Euclidean geometry began to identify shapes in nature which, because they defied conventional description, became known as 'mathematical monsters'. The German Felix Hausdorff put forward a system for classifying these patterns, but it was Mandelbrot's fractals that raised awareness of how widespread these seemingly 'unpredictable' shapes actually are.

Artificial beauty

This computer graphic was generated by a programme designed to model fractals, but in its formation of infinitely repeated patterns, it resembles forms found in the natural world, such as sea-urchin shells.

a macrocosmic scale. The list of instances in nature goes on and on: the shapes of mountain ranges or clouds, the organisation of pulmonary alveoli, the morphology of certain natural organisms and, most famously the extraordinary Romanesco broccoli.

The coasts of Brittany

The first application of fractals to the physical world took place in 1967, when Mandelbrot published an article in the journal *Science* entitled 'How long is the coast of Brittany? Statistical self-similarity and Fractional Dimension'. The Breton coast – indeed, coastlines around the world – share the same characteristic, in that whether photographed from a geosurvey satellite or from the height of just a few centimetres, their irregularity is, so

to speak, always the same. If all indications of scale are omitted from the photograph, it would be impossible to deduce the distance from which it was taken. The apparent randomness of the patterns of coastlines is, in fact, what constitutes their organising principle. As Mandelbrot put it: 'clouds are not spheres, mountains are not cones, coastlines are not circles, and bark is not smooth, nor does lightning travel in a straight line'.

Applications of fractals and IT

Even so, the majority of structures in nature are not fractals, while those that do display the characteristic of self-similarity only do so up to a point. The pure mathematical expression of a fractal was given in what came to be called 'Mandelbrot sets', which are usually plotted using computer graphics.

Yet fractals have still proved their worth in modelling possible outcomes and behaviour in systems that were once believed to be ultimately random and unpredictable, but that in fact obey scientific laws. Fractal analysis is now widely used in many areas of science, notably in meteorology, seismology, biology and economics. Fractals have also found extensive application in the arts, being used to generate remarkable abstract designs, or landscapes for movies such as the *Star Trek* franchise and for video games.

FRACTALS AND CHAOS THEORY

Chaos theory – the branch of applied mathematics that studies the behaviour of unpredictable processes, such as trends in markets or global weather patterns – was greatly boosted by Mandelbrot's description of fractals. Although these processes are deterministic, in that their future behaviour is completely determined by their internal conditions, they remain unpredictable in the long term. But fractal models at least take these parameters into account, helping researchers predict the probable behaviour of these dynamic systems.

COMBAT AIRCRAFT
Speed, power and avionics

To the untrained eye, military aircraft may seem to have changed little since the first generation of fighter jets. But appearances are deceptive: while the search for greater speed dictated aircraft design for two decades after the Second World War, the advent of missiles in the late 1960s changed the rules of the game, forcing manufacturers to devise countermeasures and sophisticated avionics.

Taking off
An F-8 Crusader being launched by steam catapult from the deck of a US navy aircraft carrier in 1959. This fighter, which saw service from 1957 to 1999, was equipped with an ingenious variable-incidence wing to give it increased lift during launch and a slower landing speed.

Between 1939 and 1945 military aviation changed beyond all recognition, as jet power replaced piston engines on aircraft and radar became the norm. This period also saw the growth of pinpoint strategic bombing, which targeted vital installations and city centres alike, and its necessary corollary, rapid interception. Over time, combat aircraft became truly fearsome weapons of war, delivering incredible destructive firepower and projecting a nation's military might in order to deter any would-be aggressor.

Raising the speed stakes

Strategic bombers fly as high and as fast as possible to evade defences, they have a long operational range to penetrate to the heart of enemy territory and return safely, and they carry heavy payloads of ordnance and fuel. The pinnacle of long-range piston-engined bomber design was the American B-29 Superfortress, which was used in the Pacific in the Second World War and dropped the atomic bombs on Hiroshima and Nagasaki. These four-engined aircraft could fly at altitudes of 12,000 metres and speeds of up to 560km/h. But as high-performance single-seat jet fighters were developed after the war, capable of climbing to high altitudes in minutes at speeds of up to 1,000km/h to intercept bombers, a pressing need arose for a new generation of fast jet-powered bombers.

With respective top speeds of 800km/h and over 1,000km/h, the American Boeing B-47 Stratojet, which entered service in 1951, and the B-52 Stratofortress (1955) plugged this gap in US strategic capability. In response, in 1954 the Russians introduced the Tupolev Tu-16 ('Badger'), supplementing the Tu-95 ('Bear') turboprop-powered heavy bomber, first deployed by the Soviet Air Force in 1952 and almost as fast at 920km/h. Both superpowers then added supersonic interceptors to their arsenal to counter the heightened bomber threat. From 1955 the Russians had MiG-19 ('Farmer') and from 1956 the Americans had

CARRIER AIRCRAFT

The Second World War underlined the vital strategic importance of aircraft carriers. Steam catapults, angled decks and a system of arrester hooks and wires enabled carrier-borne aircraft to take off and land in distances of just 200–300m. But with folding wings to facilitate storage, naval shipborne aircraft were heavier and slower than their land-based counterparts. This situation changed with the introduction of the US navy's fast Vought F-8 Crusader jet fighter in 1957, and above all its successor, the F-4 Phantom. More recently, the trend is for multi-role aircraft, such as the McDonnell Douglas F/A-18 Hornet (1983), with land and naval variants, and the versatile British BAe Sea Harrier (1978) with vertical take off and landing.

Old warhorse
The B-52 Stratofortress entered service with the US Air Force in 1955 and is still going strong. It is not earmarked for retirement until 2040.

the Convair F-102 Delta Dagger: both were capable of 1,500km/h – 1.3 times the speed of sound.

Reaching Mach-2

The years 1958 to 1960 saw jet fighters reach twice the speed of sound at altitude, raising operational ceilings to over 18,000 metres. The first of these aircraft was the American Lockheed F-104 Starfighter (1958); its rocket-shaped fuselage, stubby wings and high landing speed proved lethal to inexperienced pilots, earning it the nickname 'The Widowmaker' in West Germany. Other Mach-2 interceptors of this era were Britain's English Electric Lightning, the American F-106 Delta Dart and F-4 Phantom and the French Dassault Mirage III. Their counterparts, flown by the Soviets and their Warsaw Pact allies, included the Mig-21 ('Fishbed'), and the Sukhoi Su-9 ('Fishpot') and Su-15 ('Flagon').

Bomber development struggled to keep pace. Delivered in 1960 to the US Air Force, the delta-winged Convair B-58 Hustler was the world's first supersonic bomber with Mach-2 capability, but its high operational costs and limited range shortened its service life. The first Soviet Mach-2 bomber, the Tu-22M ('Backfire'), arrived in 1972.

The 'missile problem'

Another factor that seriously compromised the B-58's efficacy, and which in time was to spell the demise of all strategic bombers, was the advent of highly accurate surface-to-air missiles (SAMs), which could destroy aircraft however high they flew. The first warning sign came in 1960 when an American U-2 spy plane piloted by Colonel Gary Powers was brought down at high altitude over Soviet airspace by a battery of SA-2 missiles. Even the XB-70 Valkyrie, a huge, six-engined Mach-3 US bomber then in development and designed to fly at over 23,000 metres, could not escape the fact that missile performance was fast outstripping aircraft design.

Air superiority
The twin-engined, two-seat McDonnell Douglas F-4 Phantom, built between 1960 and 1981, was a fast all-weather fighter, capable of Mach 2 and more. It was exported to 11 countries, including the United Kingdom.

EYES IN THE SKY

Ever since the very early days of aviation, one of the key functions of military aircraft has been reconnaissance. The role of the spotter plane was to gather intelligence on enemy positions without being seen and without engaging opposing aircraft. The zenith of high-altitude reconnaissance was reached in the decades from the 1960s to the 1990s by the US Lockheed SR-71 'Blackbird', which could fly at Mach 3.2 at 24,000m. This role is now performed by low-orbit satellites, but aircraft continued to perform tactical reconnaissance using cameras and intelligence sensors to detect radar and radio signals. A more recent development is pilotless drones, which can stay aloft for long periods and have been used both for reconnaissance and for launching missiles against terrorist targets, notably on the Pakistan–Afghanistan border.

The Valkyrie never got beyond the prototype stage, as military doctrine moved away from high-altitude strategic bombing. The only examples of this type of aircraft still flying are the American B-1 and B-2 'Stealth' bombers, and the Soviet Tupolev Tu-160 ('Blackjack'). Likewise, though the early 1970s saw the first Mach 3+ operational fighter, the Mig-25, enter service, the era of the pure interceptor was also coming to and end.

Multi-role combat aircraft

The trend since has been towards multi-role combat aircraft, such as the Panavia Tornado (1979) and its successor, the Eurofighter Typhoon (2003). With reconnaissance roles now largely fulfilled by satellites and pilotless drones, the main types of frontline missions for aircraft are twofold. First, ground attack involves flying at low level to neutralise an enemy's military and communications assets (such as troop concentrations, tanks, missile batteries, radar installations and airfields), often in preparation for an assault by land-based forces. Aircraft performing this role are usually subsonic, ruggedly built to withstand defensive fire and carry large weapons payloads. The classic example is the American Republic A-10 Thunderbolt; it was A-10s that devastated the Iraqi forces as they retreated from Kuwait on the infamous 'Highway of Death' in 1991. The second main role is patrol and pursuit, which requires fast aircraft that must be highly manoeuvrable to engage the enemy in dogfights, yet carry enough fuel to stay on patrol for long periods.

Off the drawing board and into the air
The Russian Tupolev Tu-160 ('Blackjack') supersonic strategic bomber, the world's largest combat aircraft, was developed in the 1980s but mothballed in 1992 after the collapse of the Soviet Union. In 2005 the project was revived and a new model delivered to the Russian Air Force, largely as a gesture to proclaim a revival of Russian military prestige. The cockpit (above) carries a crew of four: pilot, co-pilot, weapons systems officer and defensive systems operator.

Seeing the sound barrier
An F/A-18 Hornet fighter from the carrier USS Constellation *breaking through the sound barrier (left). The visible pressure wave occurs when a plane is at low altitude over water: the pressure created by the forward sound waves squeezes moisture in the air to form a ball of condensation around the aircraft.*

THE MACH NUMBER

Named in honour of the Austrian physicist Ernst Mach, the Mach number denotes the velocity of an object moving through air divided by the speed of sound. It has become the standard way of expressing the performance of supersonic aircraft. Thus, a plane travelling at the speed of sound, which is 1,200km/h at sea level and just under 1,000km/h at altitude, is said to be flying at Mach 1. Aircraft with top speeds lower than the speed of sound are called subsonic, while those capable of flying faster are supersonic. Aircraft reach optimal performance at altitude, where the rarefied air offers least resistance.

French fighter
A Dassault Rafale firing decoy flares to distract anti-aircraft missiles. Introduced in 2000, this versatile aircraft will be built up into a fleet of 2,030 planes to replace a variety of types currently in service with the French air force and navy.

AREA 51 – TOP SECRET

In the Nevada Desert, near the southern edge of Groom Lake salt flat, lies the most secret military facility in America: Area 51. The installation does not appear on maps or satellite images and is protected by high-level security, including an overflight ban. The reason is that this is home to the USA's most confidential aircraft development programmes. It was here that the U-2 and SR-71 spy planes were developed, and more recently the F-117 Nighthawk Stealth fighter and its prototype, the 'Have Blue'. The secrecy surrounding the base and its testing has made it the subject of many conspiracy theories concerning UFOs.

Close formation flying
A cockpit-camera view of an Alpha Jet pilot in the Patrouille Acrobatique de France *display team over the Pyramids of Giza in Egypt. This joint Franco-German jet was designed as a trainer plane.*

Over time, roles have blurred, with fighters capable of bombing, reconnaissance and interception. This began with the F-4 Phantom, and continued with the swing-wing General Dynamics F-111 (1967). The Strike Eagle (1989) was a ground attack version of the highly successful F-15 Eagle fighter (1976). Current frontline combat aircraft such as the Dassault Rafale and the Eurofighter Typhoon are designed to switch easily between roles.

The age of avionics

Combat aircraft have come to be regarded as just part of a sophisticated weapons platform that also comprises ordnance and radar guidance. Radar started as a ground-station early warning network, but was soon installed on aircraft to fulfil both a passive (detection) and active (weapons guidance) role. While modern combat aircraft have become more difficult to fly due to inherent instability, pilots are being asked to perform an increasing number of tasks. Avionics – electronic aircraft-management systems – can help: fly-by-wire computerised flight control, head-up displays to help the pilot navigate and fire weapons, and cockpit voice-control are some innovations designed to ease the pilot's workload.

Ghosts in the sky

Sheer speed has long since ceased to be the key criteria in the development of military planes. Today, the ultimate aim for designers of combat aircraft is to create a machine that is invisible to the enemy. The 'stealth' concept, first applied to spy planes in the 1960s, is not a single technology but a combination of the fruits of cutting-edge research into materials, aircraft design and avionics.

Futuristic form
The F-117 Nighthawk ground-attack aircraft (above), a single-seat jet 20m long and with a wingspan of almost 14m. Its radar signature is equivalent to that of a pigeon.

In April 1982 the US Air Force took delivery of a new machine that bore little resemblance to aircraft past or present. Roughly delta-shaped, with curious plate-like and sharply faceted surfaces, the plane was an aerodynamic monstrosity. Yet this was their new cutting-edge ground-attack aircraft, the Lockheed-Martin F-117 Nighthawk. It was the world's first operational 'stealth' aeroplane, designed in great secrecy in the late 1970s.

A cloak of invisibility

Conventional aircraft emit electromagnetic pulses from their radio and radar, infrared radiation from the engines and sound waves both from the engines and from airflow over the wings and fuselage. Stealth technology is designed to reduce the electronic, heat and noise 'signature' of an aircraft to a minimum so as to provide as elusive a target as possible to enemy radar. The pursuit of stealth begins with the aircraft's shape: surfaces were tilted away from the normal vertical–horizontal arrangement, such as where the tail meets the fuselage, to minimise reflections that can be picked up by radar, or were made convex to deflect radar waves in all directions. Radar-absorbent coatings were used, which convert radar energy into heat rather than reflecting it back. The engines were incorporated into the fuselage to streamline the overall shape, while the jet tailpipes were disguised and moved to above the wing (most infrared detectors are ground-based, scanning the underside of aircraft). The F-117 had lower engine power thrust to reduce its heat signature and finally it carried no radar, navigating instead by GPS and inertial navigation systems.

Moving towards stealth

The story of aircraft stealth technology goes back to the early 1960s and the development, in conditions of utmost secrecy, of the Lockheed A-12 (the 'Oxcart') high-altitude reconnaissance plane. This radical plane, the forerunner of the SR-71 Blackbird, was the first to have a 'flat-belly' shape, achieved by adding chines to either side of the fuselage, flowing smoothly into the wing, which reduced the cross-section of the aircraft detectable by radar. The experience gained from the project would later help Lockheed in designing a real 'stealth' plane – the prototype of the Nighthawk, codenamed 'Have Blue'. Two-thirds the size of the F-117, Have Blue was polyhedral in shape with

'TACIT BLUE'

Over a period of three years (1982–5) a strange twin-turbofan plane, nicknamed 'The Whale' by its crews, made repeated flights from the top-secret Area 51 base in Nevada. The Northrop 'Tacit Blue' experimental surveillance aircraft was a testbed for several new stealth technologies, including a 'low probability of intercept' on-board radar, special geometry and composite materials.

The data collected from the Tacit Blue programme, which was only made public in 1996, was used on Northrop's 'flying wing' B-2 stealth bomber.

Cutting-edge
The extraordinary Northrop B-2 Spirit stealth bomber, the 'flying wing' (above). Only 21 were built, at a cost of $737 million each.

Retired spy
The Lockheed SR-71 Blackbird (right) was designed for high altitude reconnaissance. They were capable of sustained Mach 3 flight and during their service career in the Cold War, Blackbirds allegedly dodged 2,500 Russian surface-to-air missiles simply by opening the throttle and outrunning the threat. When they were no longer required for reconnaissance, NASA took three as testbeds for space technology.

State of the art
Lockheed's F-22 Raptor fighter incorporates so many new pieces of secret stealth technology and avionics that American federal law prohibits it from being built for export and sold abroad.

concealed air intakes, masked tailpipes and radar-absorbent paint. Two test aircraft were built, then exhaustedly tested between 1977 and 1979. They proved their stealth capability flying in formation with conventional fighters: only the latter were detected by radar – an observer had to be placed under the flightpath to give visual verification that the stealth prototype flights had taken place.

Budgetary constraints, plus the arrival of the new F-22 Raptor and F-35 Lightning, prompted the US Air Force to retire the F-117 Nighthawk in 2008. Unlike previous military aircraft, though, it was not mothballed at the famous aircraft 'graveyard' at Davis-Monthan Air Force Base in Arizona, but kept under guard at a special facility, as many of its technologies are still on the classified list.

Still flying

The bomber counterpart of the F-117 is the Northrop B-2 Spirit. Its distinctive 'flying-wing' profile is the result of complex computer calculations. It entered service in 1997, but the projected fleet of 132 was cut to 21 following

THE 'HUSH-HUSH' PLANE

During the Vietnam War, American forces found they urgently required an ultra-quiet aircraft to conduct low-altitude night reconnaissance of enemy positions. The answer, delivered in 1969, was the Lockheed YO-3A Quiet Star. With an aluminium fuselage based on a glider, a silenced engine and a propeller operating at subsonic tip speed, the YO-3A could fly at a height of 300m and not be heard on the ground. It was fitted with a night vision aerial periscope and a laser target detector. After the war, the Quiet Star found other roles: one was used by the Louisiana Department of Wildlife and Fisheries to combat poaching, one was used by the FBI in kidnapping cases and another served with NASA as a flying microphone.

the demise of the Soviet Union, which removed its role as a Cold War deterrent. It remains the most expensive aircraft ever built.

The US Air Force's latest fighter, the F-22 Raptor, incorporates the latest developments in stealth technology, from its trapezoidal wings and entirely smooth frame to its anti-radar coating. It is the replacement for the F-15 Eagle and is physically as large as its predecessor, yet has a far smaller radar signature. Most modern combat aircraft are now constructed using a suite of different technologies that give them low radar observability.

Looking to the future
Virtual retinal display (VRD) glasses make images on screen appear as 3-D. The visual effect is achieved by the red and blue lenses in the glasses turning rapidly on and off.

3-D television 1982

In 1928 the Scottish inventor John Logie Baird patented a system for taking images in three dimensions. His invention harked back to the stereoscope devised by Sir Charles Wheatstone in 1838, which superimposed two still images, one for each eye, to produce a convincing facsimile of the real object. Baird's technique involved filming the same scene through two cameras placed a little way apart – the same distance as between the eyes. When the images were transmitted, the viewer's brain automatically combined the images from the two cameras into a single, apparently three-dimensional one.

In 1982 television companies in the USA and Europe began experimenting with the 3-D anaglyph process for producing stereoscopic images. This involves the viewer wearing special glasses in which the left lens is red and the right lens blue; each lens filters out one of two blurry images superimposed on screen to produce one 3-D image. At this early stage, the process was not adapted to colour, but this was solved by polarised glasses. These create the illusion of 3-D images not by screening out different colours but rather through the use of polarising filters. The light from each of the two images projected onto the screen is polarised in a different direction and each lens on the glasses, similarly polarised, allows only one image through.

Electronics companies are currently working to improve the 3-D on offer by developing 'active' glasses in which each lens will be a small LCD screen. Or even better, 3-D television requiring no glasses at all.

Lifelike
A Samsung flat-screen 3-D television and viewing glasses (left).

The Swatch® 1983

With a mechanism made up of just 51 parts (compared to around 125 in a conventional watch), a plastic casing and strap, and costing just 8 Swiss francs to manufacture, the first Swatch® – a contraction of 'Swiss (Made) Watch' – went on sale on 1 March, 1983. It had been developed by a small team under Ernst Thomke, managing director of the ETA watchmaker company near Solothurn, but the driving force behind the concept was Nicolas Hayek, entrepreneur and CEO of ETA's parent company. The original template for the Swatch® was the gold 'Delirium' timepiece launched by the company in January 1979, which had the distinction of being the world's thinnest watch. The Swatch® took two years to develop, but its novelty and youth appeal enabled it to win back much of the market lost in the 1970s to the Japanese. Swatch® sales in 1984 hit 3 million and total sales now stand at around 333 million.

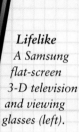

THE DISPOSABLE WATCH

The 'Timeflex' watch was invented in 2006 by two Belarussian designers, Igor Solovyov and Maria Solovyoya. It is a stick-on watch in the form of a plaster, which adheres either to clothes or the skin. Its ultra-thin batteries give just a few hours of usage and it is discarded once it runs out.

Fashion statement
Inexpensive and light, the stylish Swatch®, seen here (right) in an early version, was made in all sorts of colours and special editions.

The turbosail 1983

A turbosail is a large hollow cylinder mounted on a ship's deck. It may not look it, but this radical propulsion system harnesses the power of the wind more effectively than traditional sails. It utilises the so-called Magnus Effect (see box, below): once set in motion by the wind, the cylinder generates a longitudinal force that propels the vessel forwards. In 1924 a German engineer named Anton Flettner was the first to try to use this force for propulsion. He equipped a former sail-rigged schooner, the *Buckau*, with two huge 'Flettner rotors' and two years later the ship crossed the Atlantic.

Curious vessel
In 1926 Anton Flettner's Buckau *(right), renamed the* Baden-Baden, *crossed the Atlantic from Hamburg to New York sailing via the Canary Islands. It completed the voyage in 39 days.*

Daughter of the wind
The turbosails on the Cousteau Society's yacht L'Alcyone – *the name comes from the daughter of the wind in Greek mythology – are supplemented by diesel engines when the wind drops.*

From a windmill to the *E-Ship 1*

In the early 1980s French oceanographer and explorer Jacques-Yves Cousteau revived the idea of the turbosail. In conjunction with the physicists Lucien Malavard and Bertrand Charrier, he developed an ovoid-shaped airfoil that in 1983 was mounted on the catamaran *Moulin-à-vent* ('Windmill'). This was followed two years later by the purpose-built yacht *L'Alcyone*. The two 10-metre-high computer-controlled rotors have an acrofoil area of 21 square metres and without them the yacht would use 35 per cent more fuel.

The *E-Ship 1* is a turbosail cargo vessel of 10,500 tonnes which made her maiden voyage in August 2010. Built at Kiel in Germany, the vessel can switch between her nine traditional marine diesel engines and the rotors for propulsion, with optimal efficiency monitored by on-board computers. This innovative ship represents an important first step towards reducing not only rising fuel costs but also the high carbon emissions produced by international maritime freight.

THE MAGNUS EFFECT

In 1852 German physicist Heinrich Gustav Magnus (1802–70) discovered a hitherto unknown force, produced by air flowing over a spinning body, which acts perpendicular to the direction of the airstream. His discovery was based on the insight that, as the speed of airflow increases, so its pressure decreases; the same principle explains the phenomenon of lift on an aerofoil and also the top-spin on a tennis ball as it travels through the air. To exploit the effect, a turbosail has an aspiration system of fans which creates a depression on the side facing the desired direction of travel.

'It's good to talk ...'

F ew people nowadays can imagine life without a mobile phone. Making its debut in 1983, and at first a status symbol for the wealthy and dedicated fans of new technology, the cellphone has since spread into every aspect of modern life and transformed social relationships. Thanks to specially dedicated cellphone systems, it is now possible (almost) to call anyone, anywhere, anytime, regardless of their location.

Motorola had a long track record of making radiotelephones for cars when their development team, under director of research Martin Cooper and engineer John F. Mitchell, began working on portable cellphone technology. They unveiled the world's first prototype portable telephone, the Motorola DynaTAC, in 1973. A decade later, in 1983, Motorola finally launched the DynaTAC 8000X, the first commercially available cellphone in the US. It was huge by today's

standards, made of white plastic with a short black antenna and a keypad, and weighed in at almost a kilo. It also carried a hefty price tag of around $4,000, so was beyond the means of most people. Yet this magical device heralded the coming revolution in telecommunications.

The need for a network

Mobile phones depend on a network of low-power radio relay stations, each comprising a transmitter/receiver and an aerial, widely distributed across the country to ensure that any mobile phone is always in close enough proximity to access at least one station – in practice, usually several – to pick up a signal. Each zone from which a phone sends or receives calls is known as a 'cell'. The phone identifies the nearest aerial, transmits a recognition signal called a System Identification Code (SID) on a control channel, and is then

Future fantasy
From as early as 1905, people have envisaged phones that allowed the user to move around, as this fanciful postcard of the period demonstrates (left).

THE MAST CONTROVERSY

A debate over the potentially harmful effects of mobile phones and masts shows no sign of abating. The handsets and antennas emit radio waves with a frequency of around 1800 Hz and critics fear that these may be harmful to health. As evidence, they point to MRI scans indicating 'hotspots' in the brain tissue during mobile phone use and an increase in the incidence of localised brain cancers near the ear. Champions of the mobile phone, on the other hand, argue that no epidemiological study has yet corroborated these claims and that if harmful effects do exist, they are so weak that it would take many years of constant exposure for them to become apparent.

First in the world
John F. Mitchell of Motorola with the prototype DynaTAC in New York in 1973. The company claimed that its new phone would enable callers from virtually anywhere in the city to reach any other telephone in the world and predicted that cellphones would spread across the USA within two years, but in fact it took ten years.

On call
Radiotelephones of the 1950s (left) were fitted primarily in cars belonging to doctors or members of the emergency services.

THE CARPHONE

The first radiotelephones, fitted in cars, started to appear shortly after the Second World War, mainly in taxis and some other commercial vehicles. They were so large they were installed in the boot and required so much power they could only work with the engine running. A more compact system was first developed in the early 1960s by the Swedish company Ericsson. Three years later Bell Labs introduced their Improved Mobile Telephone Service (IMTS) in the USA. In more recent years, the march of the mobile phone has largely killed off the carphone.

years, two factors dominated mobile phone development: increasing miniaturisation of the handsets, and above all legal and administrative wrangling over assigning sufficient bandwidth for the mobile service.

The phone without a network

On 3 April, 1973, John F. Mitchell and Martin Cooper demonstrated Motorola's fully functioning prototype of the DynaTAC to a crowd of journalists and onlookers in a street in Manhattan. The famous photo-call made the front page of *Popular Science* magazine and marked the beginning of the cellphone era, but in fact the phone was way ahead of a suitable network. Even though Cooper used the phone to make a call – to Joel Engel, his opposite number in Bell Labs (AT&T) – it would take another five years before the first commercial cellphone networks were up and running in the US and initially these were only on a city-wide level, aimed primarily at motorists. The first call from a handheld mobile on a commercial network was made on a DynaTAC 8000X in October 1983, the year

More compact
Motorola's MicroTAC 8900X of 1989 (above) was the first mobile phone to have a flip-up mouthpiece that folded over the keyboard. Compact enough to be carried in a pocket, it provided better voice quality by positioning the microphone closer to the speaker's mouth.

connected. Cellphone masts are linked to the landline telephone system by base stations. The idea for such a network was first devised in 1947 by the Bell Telephone Company in the USA. It was also Bell which, from 1968 onwards, developed the first cellular phone system in America, the Advanced Mobile Phone Service (AMPS). In January 1969 the company created the first commercial cellphone network when they installed a payphone in the 'Metroliner', the premium train service linking New York with the capital, Washington DC. Over the following

USA and Canada, meanwhile, had been using separate systems (IS-54 from 1990, and IS-55 from 1993), while Japan developed its exclusive PDC (Personal Digital Cellular) standard from 1994 onwards.

Towards the fourth generation

Cellphone networks have progressed through several generations, each offering better performance in terms of download and upload speeds than the last. The first analogue networks, AMPS and Radiocom 2000, could only transmit voice signals. Current 2G networks (such as GSM and its successor GPRS, IS-54 and IS-55, and PDC) are digital, which allows them to send voice signals, text messages and images with equal ease. But the download speed of 2G networks is still limited, so 3G systems – such as UMTS in Europe and CDMA 2000 in the United States – are being introduced which use the same communication protocol as the Internet. Meanwhile, telecoms companies are preparing a fourth generation.

Mobile handsets have kept pace with these advances. The early analogue radiotelephones used in cars, and also the first truly portable digital phones, could only transmit voice messages. Then in 1996 Nokia introduced the 9000 Communicator, the first handset with a keyboard which enabled users to send and receive text messages and faxes.

Nowadays, as well as transmitting voices, mobile phones can handle text messages (SMS), images, music and videos, as well as enabling their users to listen to the radio, watch television, take photos or videos with inbuilt camera functions and access the

A gadget for go-getters
In the 1980s the mobile phone became an indispensable tool of traders on stock exchanges worldwide and was soon synonymous with the 'Yuppie' generation (Young Upwardly Mobile Professionals).

that Motorola launched the model on the market. Meanwhile, Japan had set up the first automated commercial network in 1979; the Nordic Mobile Telephone, set up in 1981–2, was the first international network, linking Sweden, Norway, Denmark and Finland.

Nowadays, different mobile telephone systems coexist around the world. The one with the greatest coverage, enabling its subscribers to use their phones in the greatest number of places, is Europe's GSM ('Global System for Mobile Communications'). First set up in 1982 GSM gradually expanded to serve Europe, Asia, Africa and the Middle East, before entering the United States in 1995. The

---

SATELLITE PHONES

Since it is clearly impossible to erect radio masts in mid-ocean or on mountain-tops, cellphone networks are of no use whatever to a wide range of people, including sailors (professional and amateur), oil-rig workers, radio and TV reporters in remote locations, forestry workers, mountaineers and others. The solution is the satellite phone. More powerful than mobile phones, these devices use signals from telecommunications satellites linked to ground relay stations, which in turn are connected to landline and cellphone networks. The starting point for the satellite system was Inmarsat (the INternational MARitime SATellite Organization), a global radio communications network created in 1979 for use by shipping, which has four satellites in high Earth orbit (36,500km above the planet's surface). Several regional satellite phone providers now exist around the world, including Terrastar (North America), Thuraya (Middle East, Africa and the Mediterranean) and AceS (Asia). The latest systems, such as Iridium and Globalstar, tap into clusters of smaller satellites (66 and 48 respectively) in low Earth orbit.

From the ends of the Earth
American Antarctic explorer Norman Vaughan uses a satellite cellphone to call from Patriot Hills base camp.

MOBILE DOWNLOAD SPEEDS

The GSM system, a 2G (second generation) mobile phone system, offers a theoretical download speed of 24.7Kbit/s (in practice, more like 9.6Kbit/s). This increased to 171.2Kbit/s (actually more like 50) with the 2.5G GPRS system. The 3G UMTS system is a huge leap forward, offering 1.92Mbit/s (384Kbit/s), while the fourth generation is anticipated to reach 100Mbit/s.

Internet. The most advanced smartphones, with 3G functionality, are more like portable computers than straightforward mobile phones. And in the not-too-distant future cellphones are set to become the only multimedia device a person will need, replacing the telephone, digital camera, radio and television receivers, laptop computer, electronic diary, digital music player and games console.

Changing the way we work and play

The 1990s saw an explosion in the mobile phone market, which has had a profound effect on both work and social arenas, blurring the boundaries between professional and private spheres. From being expensive status symbols among movers and shakers in the business world, mobiles have become an indispensable consumer product, especially among young people. In the developed world, the vast majority of people now have a mobile, while developing countries are catching up fast and the mobile has freed some countries from the need to develop costly landline telephone systems. There are now estimated to be no fewer than 4 billion individual subscribers around the world. Even taking into account the fact that some people will have more than one active subscription, this represents more than half of the world's entire population.

Keeping in touch
With 811 million individual subscribers as of March 2011, India is the world's second largest market for mobile phones, just behind China.

Mobile generation
The younger generation have made the mobile phone their own and are completely attuned to having on-going dialogues with friends by text message. Children as young as five regularly use this mode of communication.

The mobile phone

The mobile phone, or cellphone, represents the marriage of two late-19th century inventions: the radio and the telephone. But it was only in the last quarter of the 20th century that advances in electronic components and battery technology made the mobile possible.

Rotary dial of a 1930s phone

DIALLING
FROM THE DIAL TO THE KEYPAD

The first automatic telephones that enabled users to select the number they wished to call appeared at the end of the 19th century in the form of a movable rotary dial with numbers (from 0 to 9), as well as letters (in groups of two or three under each number) which identified the telephone exchange. The first phones with keypads came in 1972, with the numbers and letters rearranged in a block. The letters were retained even though they no longer had a function in connecting a call, but they were to find a new role in SMS of text messaging. The latest trend is to dispense with keys in favour of a tactile screen.

THE TELEPHONE
LONG-DISTANCE CONVERSATION

Alexander Graham Bell's invention of the telephone in 1876 gave people another way to communicate over distances in addition to letters and telegrams: for the first time, people could speak to each other. It works by transforming the human voice – a sound vibration in the air – into an electrical impulse by means of a microphone, a sensitive membrane that activates a system generating a current. The current is transmitted through a conducting wire to a receiver, which turns the signal back into sound via a loudspeaker. It was necessary to create a global network of wires, with exchanges to connect users, each of whom was apportioned a unique telephone number.

An early telephone receiver, made by the French Picart Labas company in 1910

POWER SOURCE
EVER SMALLER BATTERIES

The first radiotelephones were fitted in cars, but they used up so much energy that car batteries could not provide enough power without the car engine running. Phones only became truly portable with the advent of compact rechargeable batteries. Early mobiles used nickel-cadmium batteries, which were based on a principle first devised by the Swedish chemist Waldemar Jungner in 1889. Banned in the 1990s because of their toxicity, they were replaced first by lithium-ion batteries and then lithium polymer, introduced by Sony in 1991.

A mobile phone battery (left)

The battery indicator on an early Apple iPhone

A SIM-card (right); integrated circuits mounted on a printed circuit

COMPONENTS
FROM THE VALVE TO THE MICROPROCESSOR

The first radiotelephones for cars were bulky transmitter/receivers using vacuum tubes. In 1947 William Shockley, John Bardeen and Walter Brattain of Bell Labs invented the transistor. Small, solid, light and energy-efficient, the transistor revolutionised electronics and radio sets and radiotelephones became far smaller. In 1958 Jack St Clair Kilby of Texas Instruments and Robert Noyle, co-founder of Intel, separately devised the integrated circuit. In 1971 Intel launched its first microprocessor, the 4004 – the equivalent of an integrated circuit on a silicon chip. This was the real breakthrough that led to the development of truly portable phones, by Motorola, and other devices. SIM-cards in mobile phones also contain a tiny microprocessor, separate from that in the actual phone.

The Nokia 1011 of 1992

RADIO TRANSMISSION
FROM WIRES TO CORDLESS

Using a telephone or the telegraph involved a landline linked to a central network. But before long the problem arose of how to transmit information from and to areas not connected to the network, or from vehicles. In 1894 Guglielmo Marconi came up with a solution: wireless telegraphy, using radio waves, radio transmitters/receivers and aerials. But like the telegraph that preceded it, the wireless telegraph could only send short pulses of letters in Morse code. Wireless transmission of the voice, which required continuous wave modulation, was invented in 1900 by Reginald Aubrey Fessenden. This signalled the birth of radio, but right from the outset there were clashes between broadcasters trying to transmit on the same frequency, so governments soon took on the role of assigning radio wavebands.

A mobile phone relay mast

MESSAGES
FROM ANALOGUE TO DIGITAL

The earliest telecommunications systems used analogue signals. The sound of a person's voice was transformed into an electrical current or radio wave that was retranscribed into sound on arrival at the receiver. Any distortion during transmission could scramble the message. In 1948 the American mathematician Claude Shannon demonstrated that all information can be expressed in the form of binary numbers. A physical quantity such as sound could be measured several thousand times per second and each reading – an agglomeration of numerical values – transcribed into binary code. All that was required to transmit each piece of information was to send two short, separate base signals (the 0 and 1 of the binary code). These signals would remain intelligible whatever the vagaries of transmission, preserving all information in the message. All cellphone networks from the second generation onwards have been digital, which can carry both sound and images with equal ease.

A Sony Ericsson phone with camera and video function

MOBILE PHONES OF THE FUTURE
EXPANDING CAPABILITIES

While the first two generations of cellphones used communications systems that were specific to mobile telephony, 3G systems are based on the Internet Protocol (IP), which enables far larger amounts of data to be transmitted. This development was driven by a simple logic: since mobiles already performed like mini-computers, why not give them the capacity to connect to the Internet? As a result, mobile phones have evolved into universal tools, combining telephone with computing functions and acting as cameras, games consoles, radio and TV receivers, GPS beacons and more. The fourth generation is set to extend the capabilities of mobile phones still further.

The Nokia N97 MiniGold, a limited-edition smartphone covered in a layer of 18-carat gold and launched in 2010

Artificial skin 1984

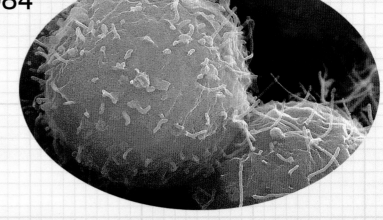

In 1984 two brothers aged 5 and 6 were admitted to the Boston Children's Hospital in the USA with severe burns over 80 per cent of their bodies. So extensive were their injuries that the normal procedure for treating serious burns victims – which involved taking undamaged patches of skin from elsewhere on the patient's body for grafting onto the burned areas – could not be applied.

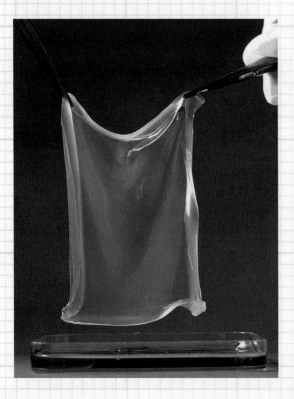

Repair patch
The tough outer layer of the skin, the epidermis, is made up of epidermal cells. When cultured in a laboratory under the correct conditions (usually in the patient's own blood plasma), these human cells form epidermal strips, like the one above, that can be used to treat burns or skin diseases such as vitiligo, a pigmentation disorder.

The surgeon in charge, Dr John Remensnyder, contacted Howard Green at Harvard Medical School, formerly of the Massachusetts Institute of Technology (MIT). Green and his team were renowned for having developed, in 1975, an effective procedure for growing keratinocytes *in vitro*. These cells form the main constituent of the epidermis. Using their new technique

the research team had been able, within the space of a few weeks, to increase the surface area of a small skin sample by ten thousand times. Close collaboration between the research team and the surgical team in Boston made it possible to reconstruct enough skin tissue for each of the boys to ensure their survival. The healthy cells for cultivation were taken from the armpits, one of the few undamaged areas of skin, and the operation was a success.

Making new skin

Other skin reconstruction techniques followed. In 1986 the Americans John Burke and Ioannis Yannas treated severe burns victims by grafting on synthetic skin made from bovine collagen taken from cowhide and polymers from shark cartilage. These biomaterials are gradually broken down by the recipient and make it possible to regenerate even deep layers of the epidermis with the patient's own skin cells, so giving the reconstituted skin greater resilience and elasticity. Since then ongoing research has produced even more sophisticated skin substitutes. From the early 2000s, research in this area has focused on stem cells (cells that have not yet specialised, whose development can be channelled *in vitro* to form different kinds of cell) and their application has opened up a vast new realm of possibilities.

Multi-purpose cells
Stem cells (above) have enabled scientists to reconstruct all the layers of the human skin – epidermis, dermis and hypodermis – along with other skin components such as sebaceous and sweat glands.

FROM SURGERY TO COSMETICS

Aside from their use in reparative surgery, skin cultures created *in vitro* (literally, 'under glass') have also proved a useful tool in studying the healing of scar tissue, the ageing process and certain illnesses, such as melanoma, or malignant skin cancer. In the cosmetics industry skin cultures are used to test the safety and efficacy of skin products, providing an ethical alternative to testing on animals.

THE QUEST FOR SPEED
Breaking new boundaries

Shrinking the planet and bringing people closer together… bestriding the narrow world like the gods and Titans of antiquity … boldly venturing into space in the footsteps of the Apollo 11 astronauts. Whatever the motivation, humans seem to have an unquenchable urge to go ever faster.

In the Chinese language the same ideogram, *kwai*, denotes both 'speed' and 'happiness'. Though this coincidence has been the case for millennia, it seems particularly appropriate in the contemporary People's Republic, where Maglev trains now hold the world speed record for vehicles running on tracks, powering the new China towards modernity and rapid economic growth.

The human desire for speed has many manifestations, not least in our relationship with motor vehicles. The thousands who turn out to watch Formula 1 and the millions who follow it on TV testify to a fascination with the spectacle of drivers pushing themselves and their machines to the limit. The Grand Prix circuit continues to expand, creating new generations of motorsport enthusiasts in countries such as Abu Dhabi, South Korea and India. We live in an age where the harmful effects of vehicle emissions on the environment are clear, yet this has done little to dent the enduring love that many people have for high-performance cars, as the huge popularity of programmes like the BBC's *Top Gear* shows.

Our shrinking planet

Perhaps this urge for speed is programmed into human DNA. The planet we inhabit is constantly moving at breakneck velocity: measured at the Equator, the Earth revolves on its own axis at more than 1,000mph (1,670km/h) and it zooms around the Sun at a staggering 107,280km/h.

Nor is it just in matters of transport that we are hooked on speed. Since the IT revolution, and especially the advent of the Internet and mobile phones with multimedia functions, instant communication has come to be expected. During the first hour of the New Year on 1 January, 2011, for example, British cellphone users sent over 100 million text messages wishing one another a Happy New Year. Many people's circle of acquaintance is now defined by the number of 'friends' they have acquired on social

Seen as it happens
Palestinians watching a live transmission of President Barack Obama's speech from Cairo on 4 June, 2009, during his first year in office.

Skimming the waves
Every year, the 'Masters of Speed' windsurfing tournament takes place in the Camargue in the South of France, attracting competitors from all over the world. Pictured here (left) is Frenchman Antoine Albeau, who in 2008 set a new world speed record of 49.09 knots.

NO MORE SEASONALITY

Who could have an objection to technology shrinking space and time? Well, market gardeners, for a start. Fruit and vegetables strictly in season are now a thing of the past for most consumers. In winter fresh green beans can be flown in from East Africa, mangetout and sugar-snap peas from Guatemala, strawberries from South America. Tomatoes and peppers are available all year round. Traditional local growers can find it hard to compete, especially if the vagaries of the weather mean that their produce is ready to sell either too early or too late. Eating habits have been changed by this move away from local seasonality and concerns are growing that the airfreighting of fresh produce around the world is creating an unsustainable carbon footprint.

Turn of speed
German speed skater Daniela Anschütz-Thoms on her way to the silver medal in the Women's 1500-metre race at the European Speed-skating championships at Heerenveen, Holland, in January 2009.

networking sites such as Facebook. The proliferation of satellite and radio links has fashioned a communications network that has transformed our world into what Marshall McLuhan, the 1960s Canadian philosopher, prophetically called the 'global village', where everything is geared towards 'abolishing both space and time as far as our planet is concerned'. Rolling news channels broadcasting round-the-clock mean that events taking place in, say, New York, Buenos Aires or Cairo are instantly and simultaneously reported in Paris, Rome, Sydney or Beijing. The era is now long gone when, for example, it took a month for

news of the assassination of President Abraham Lincoln in Washington DC to reach the west coast of the United States – or when intrepid mail pilots risked life and limb to ferry urgent dispatches to and from the far corners of the Earth over inhospitable and dangerous terrain.

The popular uprisings that swept across North Africa and the Middle East in early 2011, challenging – and in some cases overthrowing – oppressive regimes in Egypt, Tunisia, Bahrain and Libya, was driven by Internet and mobile phone contacts between young activists. Protesters around the world now use the new media to organise action against governments and other organisations, bypassing traditional channels of communication.

Pushing the envelope

Another prime mover behind the search for speed is the urge to fame and glory. The most basic form of motive power is the human body and the German athlete Armin Hary is assured his place in the annals of sprinting as the first person to run 100 metres in 10 seconds, a feat he achieved in Zurich on 21 June, 1960. Many world record-holders and half a century later, on 16 August, 2009, Usain Bolt of Jamaica ran the distance in 9.58 seconds in Berlin. Bolt's race times average out at a speed of 37.58km/h, 2.58km/h faster than Hary.

Whether performing on the track or in the pool or velodrome, athletes have prepared with ever more intensive training regimes, which has paid dividends by shaving seconds, in some cases minutes, off world speed records. One of the most sought-after cycling records, for riders of both conventional and unconventional machines, is for the greatest distance travelled in one hour. Holders of the 'conventional' one-hour record include Eddy Merckx of Belgium (49.431km in 1972) and Ondřej Sosenka of the Czech Republic (49.7km in 2005). A great deal of money, technological expertise and medical research went into contesting the world cycling speed record at altitude, which bore fruit in Mexico in January 1984, when the Italian Francesco Moser became the first rider to exceed 50km.

Still going strong
Jeannie Longo of France, five-times women's world road-racing champion, in action. In September 2009, at the age of 51, she competed in the World Time Trials Cycling Championships at Mendrisio, Switzerland.

SHAVING SECONDS

The brainchild of Italian surgeon and ergonomics expert Professor Antonio Dal Monte, the lenticular-wheeled bicycle has solid wheels in the form of two convex discs. These are heavier than traditional spoked wheels, but the extra inertia provided by the additional weight, plus their greater aerodynamic efficiency, mean that the bike can go faster. It was on a bike with lenticular wheels that Francesco Moser won the world hour record in Mexico in 1984. Since then, solid wheels have primarily been used by time-trial teams on banked velodrome circuits.

Masters of the sea
Maxi-catamarans up to 40 metres long can cut through the waves at more than 70km/h. This yacht, the Club Med, won the first non-stop, no-rules, round-the-world sailing event in 2000.

Blue streak
Donald Campbell's record-breaking car Bluebird *(below) was powered by a Bristol-Siddeley Proteus gas-turbine aero engine. In 1997 British driver Andy Green broke the sound barrier in a land-based vehicle.*

The 'absolute' one-hour record (56.375km), achieved using a bike with a special frame and equipment, has been held by Britain's Chris Boardman since 1996.

Records at sea and in the air

During the heyday of the great ocean-going passenger liners, the Blue Riband trophy for the fastest crossing of the North Atlantic by a ship in regular service was hotly contested between the flagship liners of Great Britain, the USA, France and Germany. Those glory days are long past; when the Danish catamaran-hulled ferry, *Cat Link V*, took the record in 1998 in 2 days, 20 hours and 9 minutes, the luxury *Queen Mary*, launched on the Clyde in 1936, had for years been a floating hotel moored off Long Beach, California. The world's largest passenger vessels now ply their trade on holiday cruises rather than vying for transatlantic records.

Maritime speed records today are largely the domain of specialised sailing vessels. One notable such craft is the hydrofoil yacht conceived and built by the French skipper

THE FLYING CAMPBELLS

Father and son Malcolm and Donald Campbell became famous for their record-breaking speed feats. Malcolm Campbell set nine world land speed records between 1924 and 1935, including the 1927 record of 174.88mph (281.45km/h) in his car *Bluebird*. Donald kept this famous name for his own car, which set a new record of 403.10mph (648.73km/h) at Lake Eyre in Australia in 1964. His next goal was to top 300mph on water, but he was killed in the attempt on 4 January, 1967, when his *Bluebird* boat somersaulted on Coniston Water. His body was not found until 2001.

Alain Thébault. Halfway between a sailing boat and a plane, this innovative craft is designed to go faster as it lifts out of the water; in 2008, it topped 100km/h and in 2009 set a sailing record of 51.36 knots. Yet such vessels are not built for endurance. This niche is filled by giant catamarans, such as those taking part in the challenge known simply as 'The Race', which began at Barcelona on 31 December, 2000. This round-the-world race, covering a total distance of 27,000 miles, was won by the yacht *Club Med*, captained by New Zealander Grant Dalton and Frenchman Franck Proffit, in just 62 days, 56 minutes and 33 seconds, taking nine days off the previous record.

In 1999 Bertrand Piccard and Brian Jones made a record-breaking round-the-world journey in a balloon, the *Breitling Orbiter 3*. Sealed in a pressurised cabin the size of a shower cubicle, they climbed to over 11,000m to get into the high altitude Jetstream that swirls around the Earth. During an epic flight lasting almost 20 days, they travelled more than 28,000 miles (almost 46,000km) at speeds that reached 105mph (176km/h), becoming the first men to circumnavigate the Earth in a balloon.

Voyaging into space

The adventure into space brought a whole new dimension in speed. When the Apollo 11 mission – crewed by Neil Armstrong, Buzz Aldrin and Michael Collins – journeyed to the Moon, it entered lunar orbit at a speed of

almost 40,000km/h. From there, Armstrong and Aldrin piloted the lunar-lander module *Eagle* onto the surface of the Moon, touching down on 21 July. Back on Earth, the astronauts were fêted in a huge tickertape parade in New York. Their footsteps would remain imprinted on the surface of the Moon, undisturbed by wind, as a permanent record of their achievement. Unless and until manned missions carry humans out into the depths of outer space, the exploits of the pioneering Apollo 11 mission will remain as the greatest speed and endurance adventure of all time.

Hypersonic speeds
A computer-generated image of NASA's X-43C or Hypersonic Experimental Vehicle, in action. This unmanned craft set a speed record of 12,144km/h, or Mach 9.8 – almost five times the speed of Concorde.

RECORD-BREAKING *CONCORDE*

On 12–13 October, 1992, a specially chartered flight of the Anglo-French supersonic aeroplane *Concorde*, with 48 passengers on board, circled the globe in a record time of 32 hours, 49 minutes and 3 seconds. Subtracting the time taken up by six refuelling stops in Santo Domingo, Acapulco, Honolulu, Guam, Bangkok and Bahrain, gives an actual flying time of 23 hours and 10 minutes, with an average speed of 1,744.25km/h, well in excess of 1,000mph. The flight was given the flight code AF (Air France)-1492,

to commemorate the 500th anniversary of Christopher Columbus reaching America. When *Concorde* was withdrawn from service on 24 October, 2003, it held no fewer than 180 world records. Capable of speeds of up to 2,200km/h, it remains the world's fastest commercial aeroplane. From the late 1950s onwards, experimental military jets were already breaking the Mach 2 barrier. The world's fastest jet-powered aircraft remains the Lockheed SR-71 Blackbird, which reached a speed of 3,529.5km/h in 1976.

RECORD ON RAIL

On 3 April, 2007, a heavily modified French TGV became the fastest conventional train in the world, reaching a speed of 574.8km/h.

Engineering triumph
Apart from its ill-fated copy, the Russian Tupolev Tu-144 ('Concordski'), Concorde *remains the world's only supersonic airliner. The Japanese are planning a new supersonic airliner for 2020 that could reach London from Tokyo in just 6 hours.*

Sowing seeds of doubt

In 1901 a Japanese biologist, Shigetane Ishitawa, discovered that a disease that was killing silkworms was caused by a previously undescribed bacterium. More than 80 years later, his discovery came full circle when a Belgian biotechnology company, Plant Genetic Systems, developed a strain of tobacco that could kill harmful insects by producing one of the toxic agents secreted by this same bacterium. Thus dawned the age of the genetically modified organism, or GMO for short.

1 The first step in producing a GMO is to isolate the gene of interest in a cell.

2 The gene is integrated into a fragment of DNA from another cell with a high potential for multiplying.

3 Genes are immersed in a culture medium which encourages them to multiply.

4 Several copies of the gene of interest are placed in a 'gene gun' (a biolistic particle delivery system).

5 Compressed air in the gene gun fires the particles at the target plant's cells, where certain chromosomes integrate the gene of interest.

6 The plant cells produce a new plant strain which incorporates the characteristics of the gene of interest.

Genetically modified organisms are manufactured through a process known as transgenesis. This technique involves introducing into living cells one or more genes from another organism. A gene is made up of DNA, a molecule that can be readily assimilated into a sequence of hundreds of nucleotides. When the cell reads (or transmits) the message from the gene, it produces the corresponding protein. The aim of transgenesis is to try to get the cell to produce certain proteins that have an agricultural, food or medical benefit: these are known as 'proteins of interest'. The introduced transgene only activates protein synthesis under certain conditions – for example, targeted on just one part of a plant, such as the leaves, or kicking in at a particular temperature.

Bacteria as vectors

GMOs can range from micro-organisms such as viruses, bacteria and fungi, to plant matter such as algae or higher forms of plant life, to animals. Since DNA molecules are universally present in the living world, along with the genetic code that translates information encoded in DNA into proteins, it would

---

FRANKENSTEIN FOODS?

From the outset of genetic modification, debate has raged over the ethics of the practice and the potential risks that GM foods might pose to consumers. Opponents point to studies indicating harmful effects to the kidneys, liver and heart in animals fed on genetically modified maize fodder, or that proteins produced by GM organisms have an allergenic effect. Supporters of GM counter that no toxic effects have yet been observed among consumers in countries that have embarked on large-scale GM cultivation, such as the USA.

the University of Ghent in Belgium (led by Ivo Zaenen, Marc Van Montagu and Jeff Schell) showed that an element within the bacteria's DNA was responsible for carrying segments of its genetic material that naturally integrated into the infected plant's DNA. The element was called Ti Plasmid, where Ti stands for 'tumour-inducing'. If these segments (known as T-DNA) were replaced with genes of interest, the infection would then also transduce these into the plant's cells.

Tobacco, the first GMO

In January 1983, during a conference in Miami, three separate teams announced that they had succeeded in genetically modifying tobacco: one team was led by Mary-Dell Chilton, by then at St Louis, Missouri, in conjunction with Michael Bevan and Richard Flavell from Cambridge; another was the Ghent group; the third was a team commissioned by the Monsanto agrochemicals concern in St Louis. The following year, the first transgenic tobacco plants were grown from genetically modified cells.

The fact that the genetic structure carrying the gene of interest also includes a gene that gives the cell the capacity to resist certain

Big business
The explosive rise in the cost of cereals prompted agribusiness giants to introduce high-yield transgenetic crops. Immediate advantages to farmers in yields are clear, but one long-term price is dependence on the GM seed market as seeds cannot be collected from one year's crop for sowing the following season.

theoretically be possible to produce an animal protein in a bacterium or plant, or a vegetable protein within the cell of an animal or a micro-organism. In any event, the operation is complex, since mutated cells do not always demonstrate the expected modifications, or assume a form that allows them to become active.

In plants, the principal method for introducing transgenes into target cells exploits a freak of nature discovered in the bacterium *Agrobacterium tumefaciens* in the late 1950s by the American plant biologist Armin Braun. In the various species of plant that this micro-organism can infect, it engenders a sort of tumour known as crown gall disease. In the 1970s research teams at the University of Washington in Seattle (led by Mary-Dell Chilton and Eugene Nester) and at

Potential medical benefit
In 1997 a team of French biologists produced human haemoglobin from transgenic tobacco plants. Research has been ongoing since to translate this breakthrough into a viable medical application.

antibiotics or herbicides gives researchers a straightforward way of identifying which cells the transgene has integrated with. If the plant is grown in a culture containing this antibiotic or herbicide, only the genetically modified cells will multiply.

In fact, the first GMOs do not date from 1984 but from a decade earlier, when a team in California under John Morrow and Stanley Cohen introduced DNA from a frog into the *Escherichia coli* bacteria. Thereafter, scientists from the University of California, from the Genentech company and from Harvard University succeeded, respectively, in creating strains of *E. coli* producing the human hormones somatostatin, a growth inhibitor (1977), insulin (1978) and the growth hormone (1979). In 1981 Ralph Brinster and Richard Palmiter, together with their colleagues at the University of Pennsylvania, pioneered the transference of foreign genes into mammals; the transgenic mice they produced all expressed the gene of an introduced viral enzyme called thymidine kinase.

Huge potential

Initially, the possibilities suggested by GM plants seemed more promising than those of modified micro-organisms and animals. Researchers speculated on the potential for improving the quality of agricultural produce – by modifying the way fruit ripened, for example, or by making staple food crops more productive, less dependent on fertilisers, or more resistant to viral and fungal infections.

In 1994 a tomato in which the ripening process had been artificially retarded, the 'Flavr Savr', was launched by the Calgene company in the USA. This was the first

bioengineered product licensed for human consumption, but it turned out to be a false start: the flavour was not improved and the tomato was withdrawn two years later.

From the mid-1980s, major pesticide and seed producers such as Monsanto and Pioneer realised that disease-resistant transgenic plants threatened to compromise their market. Accordingly, they began to invest heavily in GM technology, funding research into insect- and herbicide-resistance, which henceforth became the boom areas for transgenic plant development in the 1990s and 2000s. A wide variety of GM crops were produced including maize, soya beans, potatoes, tobacco and cotton, all modified with the pesticide-alternative bacterium *Bacillus thuringiensis* (Bt). Herbicide-resistant crops included soya, maize, cotton, oilseed rape and sugar beet.

Huge uncertainties

Critics were not slow to point to the risks associated with gene transference, or bioengineering. In 1974, American

GM harvest
A combine harvester (left) cutting a crop of Bt genetically modified maize, a strain resistant to the corn borer insect. The producer, Monsanto, plans to use the technique of 'gene stacking' to introduce new characteristics to maize, including resistance to drought and herbicides, plus nutritional benefits such as the production of heathier oils in the plant.

ROUNDUP®

Launched in 1974 by Monsanto, Roundup is the world's leading herbicide. Monsanto claim that the active ingredient, glyphosate, is non-toxic when the product is correctly used. But its potentially harmful impact on the environment, along with that of the surfactant that is used to deliver it, is still a matter of debate. In addition, the increase in GM crop areas under cultivation that are tolerant to glyphosate (so called 'Roundup-ready' plants) has hugely boosted its usage. This has had the effect of also raising resistance to herbicides among several species of weeds, which could impact on crop yields in future.

Market failure
The Flavr Savr tomato, marketed under the 'MacGregor's' label by Calgene, was withdrawn in 1996, its sales fatally compromised by its insipid taste and high price.

Healthier eating?

A scientist working on the production of genetically modified seedless tomatoes (above). Researchers are currently attempting to develop tomatoes with a higher quotient of carotenoids, such as lycopene. These antioxidants are believed to play a key role in the prevention of cancers.

AN ENVIRONMENTAL THREAT

There are worries that the insecticidal toxin produced by certain GM plants may prove harmful to non-targeted species like butterflies and bees. Also the transgenes – genes that identify the modified plant cells (marker genes for resistance to antibiotics) – can be spread by pollen blowing from GM crops and land on related wild plants. The resulting hybridised plants (vertical transfer) could pose a serious threat if they squeezed out and took over from their wild parents. GM plants could also potentially cross-contaminate by getting into bacteria or fungi in the soil (horizontal transfer), making micro-organisms there resistant to antibiotics. Indirectly, therefore, herbicide-resistant GM plants could end up contributing to a rise in the use of herbicides.

geneticists called for a moratorium on research into the manipulation of DNA, which was suspected of causing cancer and creating heightened resistance to antibiotics in consumers of GM foods. A conference held at Asilomar in California in 1975 recommended that work on transgenic micro-organisms should continue with the proviso that strict guidelines defining best practice be imposed, along with strict measures to confine GMO research to laboratories. These principles were duly laid down by the American National

Concerned for the future
Greenpeace activists in Stuttgart in 2004, protesting against research into GM crops.

Parliamentary protest
Delegates from the Green parties of various countries lobby for a GM-free Europe at the European Parliament on 9 March, 2010. The protest came after a decision to authorise cultivation of the 'Amflora' potato, developed by the German company BASF as cattle fodder.

questioned whether transgenic plants really were the answer to rapid improvement of cereals.

An endless controversy?

Despite strict supervision of research and field trials, several European countries imposed a complete embargo on the growing or importing of certain transgenic plants. This position was at variance with the commercial policy of the USA and other major producers of GMOs, such as Argentina, Brazil and Canada, who brought pressure to bear on the EU through

Institute of Health in 1976. Other countries, including Great Britain and France, quickly followed the US lead.

The debate between scientists now entered the public arena, both in the United States and in many European countries, where people began to voice serious misgivings about genetic manipulation and its potentially harmful effects on the environment. In 1983 the American economist and writer Jeremy Rifkin condemned transgenic antifrost bacteria, which were supposed to protect crops against damage by late spring frosts, for the ecological dangers they posed. Other critics raised ethical and philosophical objections to GMOs, claiming that they threatened the very basis of life on Earth. Some, like the US agronomist Norman Borlaug, father of the Green Revolution,

Tell-tale sign
A test kit (above) shows whether a crop is GM or not. A single violet band means GM-free; two bands signals traces of GM.

Making it clear
Since 2003 EU regulations have required food manufacturers to label products containing GM elements (right), but GM traces below 0.9 per cent do not have to be declared.

FILIÈRE SOJA
NON OGM
ORIGINE FRANCE

2x 100g

Suggestion de présentation

the World Trade Organization (WTO), citing restrictive trade practices. On the other hand, Spain has been highly receptive to GM crops, opening up 80,000 hectares to their cultivation by 2009. Other EU countries like Poland and Portugal were also in favour. By 2008, 25 countries worldwide were growing GM crops over an estimated 120 million hectares, compared to 27 million ten years previously.

Farmers wishing to grow GM plants have to put themselves entirely in the hands of agribusiness firms which retain a monopoly over the sale of seeds. GM seeds are patented and in certain countries, such as the United States, it is illegal to harvest and stockpile seed for sowing next season. So every year farmers must purchase new GM seeds, which on average cost more than traditional varieties.

The debate over GM has been sharpened by economic predictions that world agricultural production will need to increase massively – by up to 70 per cent by 2050 according to UN figures – to keep pace with population growth.

CHINA BETS ON GM RICE

In 2005 American and Chinese researchers calculated that the cultivation of two species of insect-resistant GM rice would enable Chinese farmers to cut their insecticide use by 80 per cent, while increasing their yield by 30 per cent. In 2009 the Chinese authorities gave the go-ahead for large-scale planting of a transgenic variety of Bt rice developed by the Agricultural Institute at Huazhong. By this move, the world's largest producer and consumer of rice became the first country to cultivate a transgenic strain of a staple food crop over millions of hectares. The decision was immediately condemned by environmental groups such as Greenpeace.

Cutting-edge crops
Soil-less GM strawberries (below) being grown in a greenhouse in the Netherlands. The plants have been modified with an 'antifreeze' cold-tolerance gene from Arctic flounder fish to make them frost-resistant. Right: a young shoot of genetically modified soya.

THE ECOLOGICAL MOVEMENT
Politics goes green

The 1970s saw the birth of the ecological movement in politics. Driven by concerns over the increasing harm being done to the environment, to wildlife and to people by technological advances and other human activities, 'green' campaigners began to call for a root-and-branch rethink of humankind's relationship with the natural world.

History was made in British politics on 7 May, 2010, when Caroline Lucas became the first environmentalist candidate to be elected as a Member of Parliament. The leader of the country's Green Party, Lucas had been campaigning for more than 20 years on a programme that was already familiar in the legislatures of several Western European democracies, challenging the all-out pursuit of economic growth in the light of the damage being done to the planet by commercial and technological progress. As a modern political movement, environmentalism has its roots in Germany, where activists first made the breakthrough into mainstream politics, gaining representation at state level in the late 1970s and winning 27 seats in the Federal elections of 1983. To emphasise their primary concern for nature, they called themselves *Die Grünen* ('The Greens'), a label taken up by similar-minded people in other countries.

Mass death
On 11 July, 2007, heavy industrial pollution during a period of hot weather created lethal conditions in Guanqiao Lake near Wuhan in the Hubei province of central China. Hundreds of thousands of fish were poisoned (left).

The Meadows Report

The current of thought that was known as 'ecology' in the 1970s – more usually referred to as 'environmentalism' today, to distinguish it from the scientific discipline of ecology – had at its heart the need to limit the impact that industrial society was having on nature. Such ideas had first been formulated in the 19th century, but in its modern guise environmentalism focused its activities on opposition to chemical plants and existing or planned nuclear power facilities.

A seminal work in the rise of the Green movement was a report published under the auspices of the Club of Rome, an influential think-tank then under the direction of Dennis Meadows, an American social scientist at the Massachusetts Institute of Technology (MIT). The report by Meadows and three co-authors was published in May 1972 under the title *The Limits to Growth*. It simulated the consequences of interactions between the Earth's systems and human activities, such as food production, industrial output, pollution

SILENT SPRING

American biologist and writer Rachel Carson was the first scientist to ring alarm bells with the publication of *Silent Spring* in 1962. The book documented the appalling effects that long-lasting and highly toxic pesticides such as DDT were having on the environment, particularly on bird life at the top of the food chain. Carson's work led directly to the creation of the Environmental Protection Agency (EPA) in the USA in 1970 and to the US Congress passing the first significant pieces of antipollution legislation that same year.

Pollution – bad for business

Left: A poster promoting the first Earth Day, produced by the Lower Manhattan Environment Council. The event was held in New York on 22 April, 1970, to raise awareness of environmental issues. It attracted 20 million people and thereafter was held annually.

and consumption of natural resources. Faced with a rapidly growing human population and a finite supply of resources, the scientists, economists and civil servants who made up the think-tank predicted 'a rather sudden and uncontrollable decline in both population and industrial capacity' in the 21st century. Their recommendation was 'to transform humanity into a global interdependent sustainable society, based on respect and reverence for the Earth'. The conclusion met an immediate clamour of opposition. But just 18 months later, in October 1973, a global oil crisis sharply underlined the fact that fossil fuels were not inexhaustible. It was from this point that the Green movement really took off.

Unprecedented events

Even before the oil crisis, a number of momentous events and pollution disasters had given cause for thought about whether technological progress was always a good thing. The dropping of atomic bombs on Hiroshima and Nagasaki in August 1945 shook many people's faith in science. London was known for its smogs, caused by sulphur dioxide emissions from burning coal mixing with natural fogs, but in December 1952 a particularly dense smog smothered the city for days, causing the premature deaths of some 12,000 people. A few years

later, it emerged that thousands of people living around Minimata Bay in Japan had been poisoned by mercury pumped into the sea by a chemical factory since 1932; some 900 people died and many others suffered neurological damage. In March 1967, in the first of a string of incidents involving new oil 'supertankers', the *Torrey Canyon* ran aground and broke up on the Scilly Isles, polluting large stretches of the Cornish and Breton coasts.

Rising black tide

On 30 December, 1999, the Russian oil tanker M/T Volganeft 248 ran aground near Istanbul, Turkey, during a storm in the Sea of Marmara. According to the Turkish authorities, some 1,500 tonnes of her cargo of heavy fuel-oil escaped from the hull after the ship broke in two. Wildlife, like this cormorant (above), suffered badly as a result. Some 20 years earlier, on 16 March, 1978, the supertanker Amoco Cadiz (below) was wrecked off the coast of Brittany with similarly devastating effects on local wildlife.

The Bhopal victims
On 3 December, 1984, a huge toxic cloud of the lethal chemical methyl isocynate was accidentally released from the Union Carbide pesticide factory at Bhopal in central India. At least 3,000 people died and 600,000 were permanently disabled.

Among Green politicians, still few in number, such events confirmed the analysis of those who criticised the undue influence of science and technology on the world. More importantly, beyond these limited circles, the succession of catastrophes raised awareness among the public about environmental issues.

Concerns were heightened in the 1970s and 1980s, as more ecological disasters struck: a chemical accident at Seveso in Italy in 1976 poisoned the region with dioxin; the wreck of the *Amoco Cadiz* off Brittany in 1978 polluted miles of coastline; a nuclear reactor at Three

Mile Island in the USA went into meltdown in 1979; toxic gases from a US chemical plant killed thousands at Bhopal in India in 1984; and in 1986 came the nuclear reactor fire at Chernobyl in the Ukraine. Yet still the attitude of traditional political parties was that this was the unfortunate price that had to be paid for economic and social progress.

High-rise city
Hong Kong wreathed in smog (right). Thanks to its status as a developing economy, China is not bound by restrictions on greenhouse gas emissions imposed by the Kyoto Agreement.

Scientific backing

The case for environmentalism has been
immeasurably strengthened by the active
involvement of the scientific community. The
terms of the political debate have changed in
the light of a general consensus among experts
that global warming is increasing as a result of
human activities. The involvement of science
in the cause of protecting the planet goes back
to the 19th century, but one of the first steps to
convert knowledge into action came in 1948
with the formation of the International Union
for the Conservation of Nature (IUCN).
Every year, this body produces a 'Red List' of
species threatened with extinction. It has also
prompted the United Nations to adopt a
number of international standards on the
environment, such as the 1971 Ramsar
Convention on the conservation of vital
wetland habitats around the world.

Another important initiative was the UN
Conference on the Human Environment held
in Stockholm in 1972, which established the

Repairing Earth

A computer artwork (right) symbolises the need to reverse damage to the planet. Some of the most pressing problems include clearing up pollution, halting desertification and glacier loss, and reducing greenhouse gases. Another major concern is deforestation around the world. In the Amazon Basin (above), the World Wildlife Fund estimates that the forest will shrink by 55 per cent by 2030.

United Nations Environment Programme. Slowly but surely, protecting the natural world began to rise up the political agenda. The first principle of the Stockholm Declaration began: 'Man has the fundamental right to freedom, equality and adequate conditions of life, in an environment of a quality that permits a life of dignity and well being...'. Twenty years later, the Second Earth Summit at Rio de Janeiro reaffirmed this basic belief.

The need for sustainable growth

In 1974 scientists first warned that a high concentration of chlorofluorocarbons (CFCs) was destroying the vital ozone layer in the upper atmosphere, which protects Earth from the ultraviolet light in the Sun's rays. This was confirmed a decade later and a consensus began to emerge on the need to balance economic development with human rights and environmental protection. In a 1987 report 'Our Common Future', the World Commission

on Environment and Development, chaired by Norwegian politician Gro Harlem Brundtland, enshrined this idea in the principle of 'sustainable development'. By now, the known threats facing the planet were so many and varied they could only be countered by a multidisciplinary approach and science was rehabilitated as part of the solution.

Another aspect of growing ecological awareness has been the gradual conversion of many people to a philosophical line of thought known as environmental ethics, first voiced in North America in the 1970s. The guiding principle is that Western thought has traditionally – and wrongly – regarded other living species as having value only in so far as they are useful to human beings. According to environmental ethics, all species have an intrinsic value irrespective of usefulness.

RAISING THE TEMPERATURE OF DEBATE

In 2007 the British author and environmental activist Mark Lynas published *Six Degrees: Our Future on a Hotter Planet*, in which he delivers a clear but frightening analysis, solidly based on the science of climate change, of the consequences of a progressive rise in mean global temperatures. Projected environmental disasters include the destruction of coral reefs and the Amazonian rainforest, plus the mass extinction of species poisoned by methane gas released from melting permafrost layers. At 5–6 degrees warmer, the tropical and subtropical regions of Earth would become uninhabitable for humans, triggering mass migrations on a scale never seen before.

The hole in the ozone layer 1984

In 1970 the Dutch chemist Paul Crutzen demonstrated how nitrogen oxide (NO) and nitrogen dioxide (NO_2) react catalytically with ozone to deplete the ozone content in the atmosphere. Two years later an American researcher, Harold Johnston, identified one source of nitrous oxides in the stratosphere as supersonic aircraft, but in 1974 two chemists, the American Frank Sherwood Rowland and the Mexican Mario Molina, suggested another cause: chlorofluorocarbon gases. Known as CFCs for short, these had been widely used since the 1950s as a refrigerant, a solvent and a propellent in aerosols. Rowland and Molina proposed that these could reach the upper layers of the atmosphere, where they decomposed in the ultraviolet radiation from the Sun, releasing their chlorine atoms and accelerating the breakdown of the ozone layer. Their hypothesis was confirmed in the mid-1980s. In 1984 a Japanese scientist, Shigeru Chubachi, working at his country's Syowa Antarctic research station and using a device that could measure UV radiation absorption, found that a drastic thinning had taken place in the ozone layer during the spring of 1982.

Dwindling annually

The next year, Joe Farman, Brian Gardiner and Jon Shanklin of the British Antarctic Survey compared ozone-count and CFC-level data collected above Halley Bay from the period 1957–73 with that from 1980–84. They found that, since 1975, the ozone layer over the

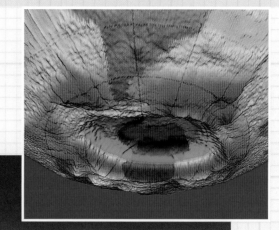

Ozone depletion
A 3-D image of the 'hole' in the ozone layer (the blue area in the centre). The hole reached its greatest extent at the end of September 2006, when people living in the southern Chilean settlement of Ushuaia had to take special precautions against UV exposure.

ER-2 18 km

Concorde 15 km

Boeing 737 12 km

Harmful hole
The Earth's protective ozone layer, which absorbs most of the Sun's ultraviolet (UV) radiation, occurs at an altitude of 14–24km above the surface of the planet, but is most concentrated at 17–21km, represented here (left) as a white layer. The hole in the layer allows UV through to the surface of the planet, shown here as a purple cloud descending on Antarctica. The altitudes are given for a Boeing 737 (12km), Concorde (15km), and the ER-2 research plane (18km) used by NASA to investigate the hole.

THE VITAL PROTECTING VEIL

Around 90 per cent of terrestrial ozone is found in the stratosphere, the layer of the atmosphere situated between 12 and 50km above the Earth's surface. Ozone, which has the chemical symbol O_3 because it comprises three atoms of oxygen, is continually produced there by the action of the sun's rays on oxygen molecules. At the same time, it is broken down into oxygen (O and its diatomic allotrope O_2) by absorbing short-wavelength, high-frequency ultraviolet light (UV-B and UV-C), forms of radiation that damage the genetic material (DNA) in living cells. Without the ozone layer life would not exist on Earth.

Southern Hemisphere had been thinning by 3 per cent a year during spring and summer (October–March), and that this was almost certainly the result of CFC emissions. Two years later, research finally confirmed that CFCs were indeed the root cause of the periodic 'hole'. Thereafter response was rapid. The Montreal Protocol, signed by 24 countries in 1987, resolved to phase out use of CFCs by 1 January, 1996, along with other substances that deplete the ozone layer. In 1995 Crutzen, Sherwood and Molina were awarded the Nobel prize for chemistry for their work in first highlighting the danger.

MEDICAL IMAGING
Making the body transparent

The latest generation of medical imaging equipment allows doctors to examine inside patients' bodies with microscopic precision. Some devices can even be used during surgical operations to guide the surgeon's hand. And all this barely a century after Wilhelm Röntgen's first X-ray plates revealed the bones inside his wife's hand.

Examining the heart in three-dimensional images ... travelling through the colon in search of minuscule tumours without recourse to a coloscopy ... diagnosing a malformation in the brain then simulating a surgical procedure on screen to find the best method of removing it so as not to cause harm. The range of imaging techniques now available – including echography, CT scanning, MRI (magnetic resonance imaging), scintigraphy, and positron emission tomography – enable doctors to study inside living human organs and tissue. Functional MRI (fMRI) scans can even be used to image the activity of an organ like the brain in real time.

Alongside the advances brought by miniaturisation and computerisation, imaging techniques have also become faster and, in the case of those that use radiation, much safer. Scientists are now talking in terms of nano-imagery, on the scale of millionths of a metre. Medical research teams are working on developing nano-probes that could investigate and target individual cancer cells: injected into the affected person, these would reveal the presence of a tumour by emitting either a radioactive or optical signal that would be picked up on a monitor screen.

Camera in a capsule

Some organs can be examined inside the body through the technique of endoscopy, in which a tube is introduced either through a natural orifice, such as the mouth, or by means of a surgical incision through the abdominal wall (laparotomy). The endoscope is linked to a minicamera and can be used to explore the alimentary canal, the respiratory tract, the genito-urinary systems and the joints. During the examination, the doctor also has the option of taking tissue samples to analyse the nature

Clean bill of health
An image of a healthy adult skeleton (right) obtained by bone scintigraphy.

Cutting-edge
Videocapsules like the device below, measuring just 26 by 11mm, are used to examine the digestive system. The camera sends 2–8 images a second through a radio transmitter to a computer.

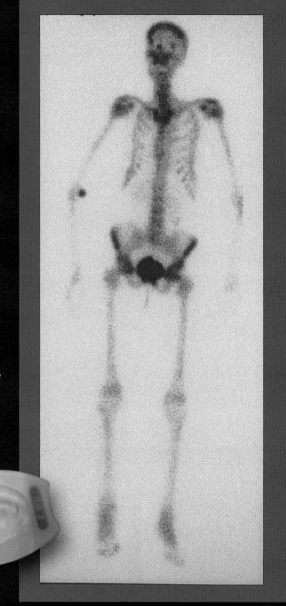

SCINTIGRAPHY

Nuclear medicine using radioisotopes began in the 1930s with the first exploration of the thyroid gland using radioactive iodine-123. Twenty years later, the American electrical engineer and biophysicist Hal Anger made a major contribution to this field with his invention of the gamma camera. This device detects radioactivity in the form of gamma rays emitted by radioactive isotopes introduced into the patient's body as tracers. In scintigraphy the camera plots the source of the radioactive gamma rays to form two-dimensional images. The technique can be used to investigate a wide range of organs including the lungs, heart, thyroid, salivary glands and bones.

Inside view

The waterproof camera in an endoscope has its own lighting system. This image (below) shows part of the interior (lumen) of a normal human small intestine.

Spotting trouble

An endoscope tube (coloured green in this X-ray image) can be used to detect and remove stones in a patient's gall bladder (the orange blob). Part of the spine and ribs are also visible in this frontal view.

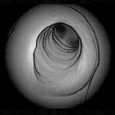

Heart check

Angiograms, like this one (left) of the carotid artery, are taken after injecting a contrast agent. This allows potential anomalies to be identified.

THE RISK FACTOR

Although X-rays help to save countless thousands of lives every year by spotting early signs of serious illness, the X-rays used in medical imaging, from radiography to mammograms and CT scans, are not without health risks, both for the patients concerned and for the medical staff operating the equipment. Ionizing radiation in high doses can cause acute damage to the skin (radiodermatitis). Over a span of several years or decades, they can cause cancers to develop as a result of the mutations they engender in cell DNA. In the early days of X-ray treatment, before the dangers were fully understood, many radiologists and technicians contracted cancers. Strict precautionary guidelines have been drawn up since for medical professionals and the radiation doses used have been drastically reduced to minimise the danger to patients. Even so, the risk of X-ray-induced tumours has not been entirely dispelled.

of any lesions or abnormalities discovered, or can even carry out keyhole surgery there and then. Since the early 2000s, an even more advanced form of endoscopy has been introduced for studying the digestive system: the videocapsule, a tiny device fitted with a sophisticated camera. Swallowed like a tablet, the videocapsule can travel down the entire length of the digestive tract over the course of several hours, exploring in particular the small intestine – the long section of the intestine just before the colon – which hitherto was largely inaccessible.

The cardiovascular system is still studied by means of X-rays, after injection of an iodised contrast agent that circulates through the blood vessels. The technique, known as coronarography, is still the most widely used

CT scanning

A patient about to undergo a CT scan. X-ray scans are taken simultaneously from various angles around the patent's body, then combined by a computer to produce cross-sectional images of the organs under investigation.

Vivid image

A 3-D scanner image of a human heart (above). The resolution is so sharp doctors can zoom in on a particular detail to identify a tumour or other damage that a simple X-ray would miss.

technique for X-raying coronary arteries, the vessels that pump blood to the heart, but is increasingly being supplanted by MRI and other forms of scanning.

An image in 10 seconds

Medical imaging and endoscopies have enabled doctors to read the human body like a book. The choice of the precise technique is determined by a variety of factors, including the organ to be examined, the type of illness suspected and the condition of the individual patient. A pregnant woman, for example, can safely undergo an MRI scan, but cannot be subjected to X-rays.

With early CT scanners in the 1970s, it took several minutes to capture an image and several hours of computer work thereafter to process it. The latest devices can scan a patient's entire body in less than 10 seconds, with a precision approaching the order of tenths of a millimetre. This remarkable progress is due in part to advances in data processing, but the design of the machines has also evolved considerably over the years. In place of just one X-ray tube, fast scanners now have two, which can be rotated around the patient simultaneously at high speed.

The use of CT scanning machines has become almost routine in the diagnosis of tumours, deformities and fractures. The latest devices are particularly efficient at examining the coronary arteries and producing virtual endoscopies of the gastro-intestinal and respiratory systems. Yet this technology still has the disadvantage of exposing patients to radioactivity – unlike MRI scans, which works through electromagnetic pulses generated by a powerful magnet.

DIGITAL MAMMOGRAPHY

The German surgeon Albert Salomon, who published his results in 1913, was the first to study a series of X-ray images alongside breast tissue removed from some 3,000 mastectomy patients. Modern methods can reveal the presence of small tumours, either benign or malignant, long before they become clinically apparent. The technique entails compressing the breast and exposing it to a weak dose of ionizing radition. Digital units have been used for some years now: instead of being captured on plates or film, as with conventional mammograms, the images are shown directly on a high-resolution computer screen.

THE INCREASING POWER OF MRI SCANNERS

Since their inception more than 30 years ago, in 1977, magnetic resonance imaging (MRI) scanners have grown steadily in power. This improved performance derives in part from an exponential increase in the intensity of the magnetic field, which is measured by the SI unit of teslas (T). In the early 1980s, the strongest field that could be generated was less than 0.5T (or 10 times the strength of the Earth's magnetic field). Today, most scanners operate at an intensity of 1–3T. These so-called 'high-field' or 'very high-field' MRI scanners (above 3T) are mainly used for studying the brain, chest, abdomen, blood vessels and heart.

Some medical research institutions have even more powerful scanners. The Sir Peter Mansfield Magnetic Resonance Centre in Nottingham has a 7T scanner, which is used as a national resource for functional Magnetic Resonance Imaging (fMRI) of the brain. The most powerful MR imager in the world – at the Max Planck Institute for Biological Cybernetics in Tübingen, Germany – is a small animal scanner with a field strength of 16.4T. These ultra-high-field devices are deployed in a variety of research programmes, including modelling brain anatomy to gain a better insight into brain diseases such as epilepsy and Alzheimer's Disease.

Brain tumour
This three-dimensional model of the head of a 43-year-old woman was compiled from numerous MRI scans (above). The cutaway reveals a large glioma tumour (in red), a central nervous system tumour that arises from the brain's glial cells. About half of all primary brain tumours are of this type.

Healthy brain
A coloured composite 3-D MRI scan image of a human brain (above). The ventricles (orange) are four cavities that circulate the cushioning cerebrospinal fluid (CSF).

Magnetic tunnel
A medical MRI scanner (above left) is equipped with a superconducting electromagnet that generates a strong magnetic field, together with auxiliary magnets that produce fields of variable strengths.

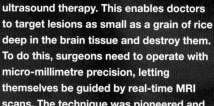

Ax 20070607

iMR-2 Ax 10:37

iMR-3 Ax 13:28

Load

Orthogonal
The syste
navigatio

Tip Exten

BRAIN SURGERY BY MRI

Neurosurgery is entering a new era thanks to the introduction of powerful ultrasound therapy. This enables doctors to target lesions as small as a grain of rice deep in the brain tissue and destroy them. To do this, surgeons need to operate with micro-millimetre precision, letting themselves be guided by real-time MRI scans. The technique was pioneered and developed by several surgical teams operating on patients suffering from chronic illnesses, such as Parkinson's disease and brain tumours. Ultrasound combined with MRI has also been used extensively by various clinical research teams, as well as for treating fibroids of the uterus and localised cancers, such as those of the prostate, breast or liver.

Precision procedure
A surgeon removes a brain tumour with the aid of functional MRI scanning. In some cases, the patient is woken in the middle of the procedure for tests to ascertain whether the brain is still responding normally. In this type of procedure, images are taken every two to six seconds.

Watching the body in action

MRI scanning is the most sensitive method of examining soft tissues with a high water or fat content, such as blood vessels. This type of examination is particularly recommended for investigating diseases of the brain and spinal cord. They can be used to perform functional examinations, such as monitoring specific active zones in the brain during certain actions or in particular states.

Medical imaging in general has become an invaluable diagnostic tool for surgeons in identifying illnesses and assessing their gravity before deciding on the most appropriate procedure to adopt. For instance, MRI scans can help to determine the best way of accessing and treating a brain tumour. In certain forms of automated surgery, the surgeon can even control his movements through a real-time MRI scan. In these cases, specially adapted machines are used, generally comprising an ultra-high magnetic field and a wider, shorter tunnel than on a conventional MRI scanner. Medical researchers are currently working on an MRI scanner that will utilise specific cell markers or biological reactions at the cellular or even molecular level. There are many potential applications for such a device, from cancer research to cardiology and the study of a range of inflammatory diseases such as Parkinson's, lupus and irritable bowel syndrome (IBS).

PET scans 1985

Positron emission tomography, known as PET scanning for short, is a form of nuclear medical imaging that emerged in American hospitals in the mid-1980s. The principle behind the technique had been known for some time: the first PET scans were conducted as early as the 1950s at Massachusetts General Hospital in Boston, on patients who were thought to have contracted brain tumours. Gradually, the technique proved its worth in a variety of other applications. It was used, for example, as a diagnostic tool, for monitoring the pathology of certain types of tumour in cancer research, and in cardiology to investigate areas of myocardial tissue that remained viable after a heart attack (infarction). PET scans also found widespread use in neurology, notably in the study of Parkinson's and Alzheimer's diseases.

A three-dimensional image

Unlike scintigraphy, which produces two-dimensional nuclear images, PET scans result in 3-D imagery. In both techniques, patients are injected with a tracer fluid to reveal the workings of the organ under investigation. This agent is marked with a radioactive isotope designed to emit positrons, particles that combine with electrons of the same mass but with an opposite electrical charge. The meeting of positrons and electrons gives rise to gamma radiation, which is detected by a positron camera. From this, the 3-D image is digitally reconstructed from the data. The tracer agent is commonly a derivative of glucose marked with the radioisotope fluorine-18, which can pinpoint areas in the organism involving heavy sugar consumption. This is the case, for example, with cancerous cells, whose metabolism is more active than normal cells.

A complete picture
PET scans can be combined with other scanning techniques to build a complete functional and anatomical picture of the patient under investigation.

IN THE SERVICE OF INNOVATION

PET scans have shown themselves to be an invaluable tool in developing new drugs, particularly for the treatment of neurological disorders. The technique enables researchers quickly and precisely to pinpoint the distribution of a particular molecule within the organism, its ability to act on a predetermined target and to see the way it acts. In some cases, the examination can even measure the specific efficacy of a drug prior to clinical trials, by monitoring the evolution of biological indicators of the disease.

Confronting a killer

In the early 1980s medical research teams in the USA and Europe were engaged in a desperate race to identify the virus that causes AIDS. Despite the investment of huge resources, the worldwide scourge of this deadly disease has proved hard to control. Twenty-five years after it was first described, AIDS is still widespread, especially in the developing world.

Universal symbol
The red ribbon was conceived as a symbol of the fight against AIDS by the New York artist Frank Moore.

A new threat
The illustration shows tiny AIDS virus particles (above, on the left and top right) with four types of white blood cell (leucocytes). The large macrophage (top centre) and a helper T-cell (bottom left) are under attack by the particles. The B-lymphocyte (bottom right) is a precursor to red plasma cells (centre right). The plasma cells produce the red Y-shaped antibodies that bind to HIV-infected cells.

In June 1981 the Center for Disease Control in Atlanta, Georgia, became aware of a mystery illness affecting homosexual men. Normally harmless infectious agents were triggering extremely serious diseases such as a rare form of pneumonia and a cancer known as Kaposi's sarcoma. Those affected were all found to be suffering from a total collapse of the immune system. The press immediately dubbed this alarming new epidemic the 'gay syndrome' and speculated that the disease might be contagious. But by 1982 cases were also being found among heroin users and haemophiliacs, pointing to the exchange of infected bodily fluids, such as blood or ejaculate, as the most likely mode of transmission. Accordingly, the acronym AIDS, short for Acquired Immune Deficiency Syndrome, was coined for the illness. AIDS appeared to be caused by a virus, but scientists were initially unable to pinpoint

which. Retroviruses – that is, viruses with a gene pool comprised of RNA (ribonucleic acids) rather than DNA (deoxyribose nucleic acids) – seemed likely suspects, since some of these had already been identified as triggering immunodeficiencies in cats.

Barking up the wrong tree

In December 1982 a number of leading French clinicians, including Willy Rozenbaum and Jacques Leibovitch, joined the viral oncology unit run by Luc Montagnier at the Pasteur Institute in Paris to try to identify the new killer disease. A team specialising in the role played by retroviruses in cancers, under the direction of Jean-Claude Chermann and his deputy Françoise Barré-Sinoussi, embarked on intensive research. Isolating the infectious agent responsible for the disease proved difficult, since the count of T4 lymphocytes, the immune cells that seemed to be its target, plummeted in people who had contracted AIDS. Because the researchers suspected that one of the early signs of the disease was lymphadenopathy – the swelling of the lymph nodes that contain the T4 lymphocytes – they carried out a biopsy on

FROM HIV TO AIDS

Infection by the human immunodeficiency virus, which can occur without the person being aware, may eventually manifest itself in an acute retroviral syndrome whose symptoms include fever, joint pain and swelling of the lymph nodes. If left untreated, within 5 to 15 years this condition can develop into AIDS, where the T-4 lymphocyte count falls below 200 per cubic mm of blood. Clinical stage 1 of HIV infection is characterised by nothing more than a persistent swelling of the lymph nodes. Stage 2 is accompanied by slight weight loss, recurring respiratory infections and minor skin and mucous membrane complaints. Opportunistic diseases (including chronic diarrhoea, Candida and TB) multiply in Stage 3 and especially in Stage 4, where 22 AIDS-related opportunistic infections and cancers have been identified. Multi-pronged therapy can now slow down the progress of AIDS and with prompt treatment life expectancy is, on average, 30 years after diagnosis.

Going public
*In June 1983
some 1,500 people
assembled in New
York's Central Park,
to remember those
who had already
died of AIDS.
People on the vigil
(left) held up
placards, each
bearing a number
representing an
AIDS victim in the
USA. This was
the first campaign
to raise public
awareness of the
growing epidemic.*

the lymph nodes of a patient presenting these symptoms, in the process detecting a virus that was possibly the one in question.

To help identify the virus, the French researchers approached a team working under Professor Robert Gallo at the National Cancer Institute at Bethesda in Maryland. In 1980 this eminent biomedical researcher and his colleagues had described the first known human retrovirus, HTLV-1 (Human T-Cell Leukaemia Virus). Gallo thought it possible that HTLV-1 might be the root cause of AIDS,

but initial comparisons with a sample from France soon scotched this theory.

In the May 1983 issue of the journal *Science*, the French published the first description of their virus, which they called Lymphadenopathy Associated Virus, or LAV. But the causal link between the LAV virus and AIDS still remained to be proved. Research intensified over the next few months as the medical teams characterised the virus, analysed the proteins it produced and developed blood tests to detect it.

Steadily multiplying – the replication cycle of HIV
Glycoprotein spikes on the viral envelope (1) penetrate the cytoplasm of a T-lymphocyte white blood cell (2) and introduce the genome of the virus – a single strand of RNA – into the cell. This is transcribed into a double strand of DNA (3), which can integrate with a host-cell chromosome (4). The virus then hijacks the cell's nuclear machinery, causing it to produce viral RNA molecules and proteins (5). These work free of the host cell (6, 7, 8) and go in search of more healthy cells to infect (9).

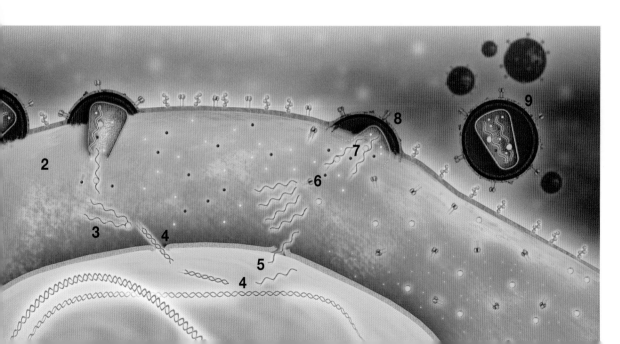

Gallo versus Montagnier

Meanwhile, in the United States, Gallo's team had identified a second human retrovirus, HTLV-2. They were working with different strains of virus, some supplied by the Pasteur Institute, in the hope of showing that a virus from the same family was responsible for AIDS. In the process, they isolated a virus they thought was distinct from LAV, which they labelled HTLV-3. Then, in a dramatic turn of events in April 1984, Gallo published an article claiming that HTLV-3 was the cause of AIDS. He made this announcement to the entire world at a press conference attended by the US Minister of Health. A great deal was at stake: in particular, the patenting of screening tests for AIDS sparked a major legal battle. The US government refused, for example, to patent an LAV test devised by Montagnier and his colleagues, but approved Gallo's equivalent HTLV-3 test.

But things were set to change. The sequencing of the LAV virus, completed in January 1985, indicated that it did not belong to the HTLV-1 family. And HTLV-3, after being sequenced in its turn, turned out to be very similar to LAV, disproving Gallo's assertion. An agreement was finally published in March 1987 sharing the credit for the discovery of the virus between the Pasteur Institute and the Bethesda National Cancer Institute: LAV and HTLV-3 were one and the same. The virus was renamed HIV – Human Immunodeficiency Virus. The sharing of rights on screening tests was regulated by a Franco-American intergovernmental accord. In 2008 the controversy was brought to a close by the award of the Nobel prize for medicine to Luc Montagnier and Françoise Barré-Sinoussi.

A pivotal year

In 1985 some 23,000 people were diagnosed with AIDS-related illnesses in the USA and 12,500 deaths were attributed to the disease. This compared to 1,300 people infected and 6,000 deaths two years before. Until then the subject had been regarded as something taboo and shameful. It was thought to affect only homosexuals and drug-users, which in the eyes of many made it a self-inflicted problem. But a sea-change now began in public perceptions and attitudes towards the epidemic, helped by the movie star Rock Hudson who, shortly before his death in 1985, revealed that he was HIV-positive and had contracted AIDS.

Spread by transfusions with infected blood and by sexual promiscuity, the disease was reaching pandemic proportions. Its rapid spread through developing countries was especially worrying: in some African countries, up to 5 per cent of the adult population became infected. The first international conference on AIDS was held in Atlanta, in the USA, in 1985. Beginning in the following year, the United Nations instituted a worldwide programme to combat the menace.

No boundaries
People have fallen prey to AIDS throughout the developed and developing world. This victim of the disease (below), wasted away to skin and bone, was photographed in Henan Province in China. In the early 1990s, large numbers of Chinese peasants are thought to have contracted HIV/AIDS when the authorities ran a mass campaign to attract blood donors by offering payment, but failed to implement proper hygiene practice in their transfusion centres.

CHINA'S BLOOD TRANSFUSION PLAGUE

In the early 1990s, many poor farmers in China sold their blood for cash, being given about US $5 for every litre. After the plasma was extracted from the blood for selling on, the remaining blood was injected back into donors to speed their recovery. The Chinese authorities actively encouraged participation in the scheme with the slogan: 'selling blood makes you richer, healthier and prevents high blood pressure'. But unsanitary procedures and contaminated blood led to many of those taking part contracting HIV/AIDS. Henan Province in the centre of the country was the hardest hit. China has no national compensation fund for people infected with HIV/AIDS through transfusions or blood sales.

AIDS explosion
In 2008 more than 70 per cent of new HIV/AIDS cases and 72 per cent of all recorded deaths from the disease were in sub-Saharan Africa. Many health and welfare agencies are trying to get across the message of AIDS prevention in Africa.

The race to develop anti-retroviral drugs began with therapeutic trials of AZT in the United States. This is an enzyme-inhibiting drug, which allows RNA to be retro-transcribed into DNA that can then reintegrate into the host's gene pool. First marketed in 1986, it helped to slow the HIV replication cycle, but it was both toxic and extremely expensive. That same year, a second strain of the virus (HIV-2) was isolated, giving researchers a greater insight into the mechanisms of HIV infection.

The action of HIV within the immune system and its huge variability have made it very difficult to combat. An important step forward came in 1996 with the first of the so-called tritherapies, combining three different drugs that combat the virus on several fronts.

A global campaign

Twenty-five years later, a third generation of tritherapies appeared. Yet other avenues of research, such as gene therapy and therapeutic vaccination, are still only at the experimental stage. Despite the inception of a global fund to combat AIDS and a commitment by the G8 countries to bring about universal access to treatment by 2010 – not to mention the

initiatives of individual governments and private donors – the pandemic has continued to spread. In 2008 UNAIDS recorded 2.7 million new cases and 2 million deaths worldwide, while some 33.4 million people were living with HIV/AIDS, most of them in sub-Saharan Africa. Significant steps towards developing a universal vaccine, such as that announced by Thai researchers in the autumn of 2009, provide hope that the disease will one day be stamped out, and vaccine trials have already been started with volunteers in South Africa, Rwanda and Kenya.

FIGHTING THE PHARMA GIANTS

To combat their massive AIDS epidemics, Brazil, Thailand, India and South Africa have taken on the world's large pharmaceutical companies and their patenting of prohibitively expensive anti-retroviral drugs. Campaigners rely on accords drawn up by the UN's World Trade Organization, which allow intellectual property rights to be waived in the manufacture of low-cost generic anti-retrovirals.

Stay safe
A German poster from a 2007 campaign promotes safe sex through the use of condoms (above). The picture shows condoms on various suggestively shaped vegetables, with the message 'Safe All Over the Place'. Governments have used dramatic and eye-catching advertising to persuade sexually active citizens to take precautions. A hard-hitting British campaign in the 1980s showed a tombstone inscribed with the motto: 'AIDS: Don't Die of Ignorance'.

BOOM TIME IN TOKYO
Snapshot of Japan in the 1980s

Between 1975 and 1985, the Land of the Rising Sun truly emerged from the long shadow cast by its crushing defeat in the Second World War. This was a boom decade for the Japanese capital. The rest of the world looked on in amazement – and not a little envy – as the country's economy went from strength to strength.

The Toyota Way
Workers in Toyota City (centre right), a town near Nagoya built by the Japanese car giant in 1959. With some 300,000 inhabitants, schools, a university and 12 factories, everything is geared to imbuing present and future employees with the spirit of enterprise.

Sleep tight
A guest settles in for the night at a 'capsule hotel' in Tokyo (below). In a city of limited space and a burgeoning population, such hotels were designed in the 1970s to provide affordable accommodation for businessmen.

As Western countries struggled to make headway in the tough economic conditions of the 1970s, the nation that became the shining example and model of business growth was Japan. Long regarded with suspicion, even hatred for its role in the Second World War, the country now emerged as a global leader in automobile manufacture, electronics and banking. Increasingly, the world drove Japanese cars, benefited from Japanese electronic innovations and was financed with Japanese investment.

Early birds

At five in the morning, with the neon signs of the sprawling metropolis scarcely extinguished, Tokyo wakes to begin another day of hustle and bustle. The fish market at Tsukiji is a hive of activity at this hour, as factory ships unload their catches harvested from as far afield as the coasts of Africa and Norway, or closer to home in the South China Sea and other waters around Japan. Amid the clamour in the market hall, buyers from the big restaurant chains and from small corner eateries alike come to buy fresh produce for the day's menu, be it dab, sea-bream or mackerel, or especially prized and now rare bluefin tuna for sashimi dishes. As Tsukiji quietens down, the lights begin to come on the offices of the huge skyscrapers in the Shinjuku business district.

Shinjuku's morning ritual

Behind the dazzling steel and glass façades of Shinjuku's high-rise blocks a modern

OCCUPATIONAL HAZARD

The Japanese economic miracle of the 1970s and 80s brought with it a health hazard in the phenomenon known as *karoshi*, literally 'death from overwork'. The first reported case of an occupational, stress-related fatality was in 1969, when a 29-year-old shipping manager at the country's largest newspaper group, *Asahi Shimbun*, died of a stroke. The prevailing work culture of 12-hour days, six or even seven days a week, was blamed. After several high-ranking executives with no history of ill-health died suddenly in the 1980s, the Japanese Ministry of Health began publishing data on *karoshi*, and now treats it as a separate category in mortality statistics.

Japanese ritual is played out, as the employees of large corporations (known as 'salarymen') assemble for the morning meeting that begins every working day. Any mistakes that occurred the day before are reviewed to avoid repeating them, and targets are discussed and set for the day ahead. The meeting closes with communal exercises, before everyone buckles down to do their best for their employers – which in Japan are paternalistic enterprises, rewarding loyalty with jobs for life and extensive welfare packages. Pioneered in Japan's naval shipyards in the 1920s, lifelong employment was a major driving force behind the country's economic

resurgence. Another guiding principle of Japanese management was not to recruit graduates who had specialised in a particular field, but to go for generalists instead. The thinking behind this policy was that such people were more likely to remain flexible to changes in working patterns and adapt easily to new roles, which on average are offered to employees every three years. This provided a wellspring for innovation and flexibility, both bywords for how the Japanese did business. Such adaptability even extended to staff not taking their full annual holiday entitlement – on the contrary, they would give the company their spare time for free. Until they married, employees lived in a company hostel, where customarily two people shared rooms with just 10 square metres of space.

Taking over the photographic world

This dedicated working regime helped to put Japanese companies at the cutting edge of their fields of operation. Nowhere was this more evident than in the photographic business. Fuji rose to be the undisputed world leader in camera film, Nikon and Canon cornered the market in single-lens reflex (SLR) cameras, while Olympus won millions of devotees with its compact cameras. When it started out, Fuji

was regarded with a mixture of amusement and contempt by established photographic enterprises such as Kodak in the USA, AGFA in Germany, Gevaert in Belgium and Ilford in the UK. But the Japanese company had the last laugh. In 1986 it launched the world's first disposable camera and it also anticipated digital photography way ahead of its rivals. Nikon began making SLRs in the 1960s and pioneered the autofocus function ten years later. Its cameras became the tool of choice for press photographers, who helped to popularise the brand in America and Western

Tradition and modernity
Like nowhere else in the world, Japan successfully allies long-hallowed virtues such as respect for one's ancestors, humility and a sense of duty with a modern outlook that embraces change and innovation.

CANON'S MODEL EMPLOYEES

High-flying employees of the Canon photographic company are accorded the privilege of signing machines that they assemble with their names. In the Ami plant, near Tokyo, 37-year-old Kiyomi Onda can assemble a photocopier with 1,000 components in just five hours. His colleague, 34-year-old Yuji Nakamura, put together a 2,700-component copier in under 14 hours. Canon CEO Fujio Mitarai praises his star staff as 'geniuses' and allows them to add their family names to the company's logo.

ARCHITECTURAL PLAYGROUND

Ravaged in the past by fires and earthquakes, and devastated by incendiary bombs in the Second World War, Tokyo has since become a happy hunting ground for modern architects. The capital's relaxed planning regulations foster architectural innovation. In 1961 Kunio Maekawa built the striking Tokyo Metropolitan Festival Hall in the city's Ueno Park. A 1976 addition to the city skyline was Shozo Uchida's Sompo Japan insurance building, an ultra-modern skyscraper that alludes to medieval Japanese castle design. Other iconic modern buildings include Kenzo Tange's Yoyogi National Olympic Gymnasium (1964–6) and the Nakagin Capsule Tower by Kisho Kurokawa (1972).

Fusion fashion
Japanese teen culture is a melting-pot of influences. One trend is the so-called 'Elegant Gothic Lolita' look, a fantastic blend of retro Victorian and Manga comic-book styles (near right).

Business etiquette
Japanese 'salarymen' greeting one another. There is a strict code of etiquette in Japanese commercial life. Business cards, for example, must be presented with both hands and never placed in the pocket or wallet after receipt, as this shows disrespect.

Europe. Nowadays, nine out of every ten cameras sold worldwide are made in Japan. Canon is the market leader in cameras, as well as in PC laser printers and photocopiers. Olympus went down the miniaturisation route, introducing the first mass-market compact digital camera in 1994. The firm now accounts for one in five of every compact camera sold. Even so, the company's main profits derive from its medical imaging division. Capsule endoscopes use miniature cameras developed by Olympus to explore the interior of human organs such as the stomach or the small intestine. The firm now has a 70 per cent share of this highly specialised global market.

Innovation according to Soichiro

One of the biggest names in Japanese manufacturing is Honda, a multinational concern renowned for its automobiles, motorbikes and boats. Its founder Soichiro Honda (1906–91) learned a great deal about engineering and adaptability from his father,

THE JAPANESE BILL GATES

One of the richest man in Japan is 53- year-old Masayoshi Son. The third-generation child of a Korean family in Japan, Son was imbued from an early age with an urge to succeed in business. After meeting the Japanese head of McDonald's at the age of 16, who advised him to learn English and computer science, he moved to the USA, studying at Berkeley and inventing a translation device that he sold to Sharp Electronics for $1 million. Back in Japan, he founded Nihon Softbank and Yahoo Japan. He is worth around $7 billion, but lost more money than any individual in history, some $70 billion, in the 'dot.com' bubble of 2000.

a village blacksmith who repaired bicycles and also doubled as the local dentist. After training as a car mechanic in Tokyo, Soichiro opened his own workshop in his home town, where he produced a small petrol engine that could be fitted to a bicycle. It sold like hotcakes. In 1949 he began manufacturing complete motorcycles, powered by his own 98cc engine (later upgraded to 146cc).

They may have lacked the romance of US and European motorbikes, but Honda's machines were cheap, well engineered and reliable, and they soon began to capture a significant share of the market. By the 1960s and 70s motorbikes made by Honda and its Japanese rivals Kawasaki and Suzuki were a step ahead of Western competition, both in features and pricing, and the buying public responded. It was the same story with Honda cars. At first sneered at in the West as crude and tinny, they soon impressed owners and built up a loyal following. Japanese cars began to make steady inroads in foreign markets.

Morita and miniaturisation

Meanwhile, the boss of the Sony Corporation, Akio Morita (1921–99) staked his company's future on miniaturisation in electronics. Morita was a physics graduate whose first business venture was a rice cooker he designed in 1946. In 1979 Sony launched the Walkman®, an idea Morita allegedly came up with in order to listen to his favourite music while playing golf, although another inventor would dispute this claim. The personal music player proved a

massive international hit, following on from other successes for the company, such as the pocket transistor radio (1955) and the Trinitron colour TV (1968). Sony went on to pioneer the world's first CD player (1982), the 8mm camcorder, the MiniDisc player, the 16:9 aspect ratio television, the digital camcorder and the portable phone. In terms of brand recognition, Sony is second only to Coca-Cola, a fitting testament to the dynamic march of Japanese industry in the postwar era.

Pachinko parlour
Pachinko machines, which became extremely popular in the 1980s in Japan, are gaming devices rather like vertical pinball tables. Players can win tokens, which are exchanged for gifts.

CHRONOLOGY

The timeline on the following pages records key discoveries and inventions from the early 1970s to the end of the 1980s. Selected historical landmarks are included to provide chronological context for the scientific, technological and other innovations listed below them.

1972

- Unarmed civil rights marchers are shot dead by British paratroops in Londonderry on 'Bloody Sunday'
- Richard Nixon becomes the first US president to visit the People's Republic of China
- Palestinian activists take 11 Israeli athletes hostage at the Munich Olympics; the crisis ends in a massacre

- German inventor Andreas Pavel first tests out an experimental portable music device he calls the 'stereobelt'

- Texas Instruments put the first pocket calculator on the market

- Based on work by the physicist Allan Cormack, the British researchers Hounsfield and Ambrose unveil a prototype medical CT scanner

- American mathematician and meteorologist Edward Lorenz expounds the Chaos Theory

- The Club of Rome publishes *The Limits to Growth*, a key text in the birth of the ecological movement

- Launch of the first Earth-resources satellite, Landsat 1

- A European consortium develops the highly successful Airbus A300 passenger aircraft

1973

- General Augusto Pinochet overthrows the elected Marxist government of Salvador Allende in Chile
- Yom Kippur War between Israel and her Arab neighbours provokes a four-fold increase in oil prices and a global financial crisis
- Paris Accords end US active involvement in the Vietnam War
- UK, Denmark and Ireland join the European Economic Community

- American chemist Paul Lauterbur obtains the first images through nuclear magnetic resonance scanning

- IBM launches the 3340, the first hard disk for a computer

- In the USA, Frank Nasworthy starts the craze of skateboarding by fitting polyurethane wheels to a board

- German firms Bosch and Teldix GmbH develop the antilock braking system (ABS) for cars

- NASA puts the world's first space station, Skylab, into orbit

► Ventricles of the brain, as seen on an MRI scan

▲ A patient entering the tunnel of an MRI scanner

► A camera with autofocus

1974

- US President Richard Nixon resigns over the Watergate scandal and is succeeded by his vice-president Gerald Ford
- President Juan Perón of Argentina dies and is succeeded by his widow Isabel
- The Carnation Revolution in Portugal ends decades of dictatorship and puts the country back on a democratic path

- Californian cycle-sports enthusiasts develop the all-terrain bike (ATB), first invented by the Briton Geoff Apps in 1968

- Discovery of the early hominid 'Lucy' in Ethiopia gives scientists more information on human evolution

- Hungarian architect Erno Rubik develops the Rubik's Cube

- In the United States, General Motors introduces the catalytic converter to reduce noxious exhaust gases

- French inventor Roland Moreno devises the smart card with a microchip

- American astronomers Russell A. Hulse and Joseph H. Taylor observe the first binary pulsar in the Aquila constellation

1975-6

- Death of General Franco ends dictatorship in Spain (1975)
- The brutal four-year regime of Pol Pot and the Khmer Rouge begins in Cambodia (now Kampuchea, 1975)
- Fall of Saigon and surrender of South Vietnam (1975)
- Death of Mao Zedong and Zhou Enlai in China (1976)
- Harold Wilson resigns as British Prime Minister (1976)

- Scottish researchers Hans Kosterlitz and John Hughes publish an article in the journal *Nature* on their discovery of endorphins

- German surgeon Andreas Gruentzig experiments with a new technique for treating narrowed arteries to prevent heart attacks; the technique will become known as coronary angioplasty

- American computer programmer Ray Kurzweil devises groundbreaking software for optical character recognition and speech synthesis

- First commercial flight of Concorde

◀ An audio cassette tape, as used in early personal stereo systems

▲ Sony's groundbreaking TPS-L2 Walkman®, launched in 1979

▼ A surgeon performing a coronary angioplasty

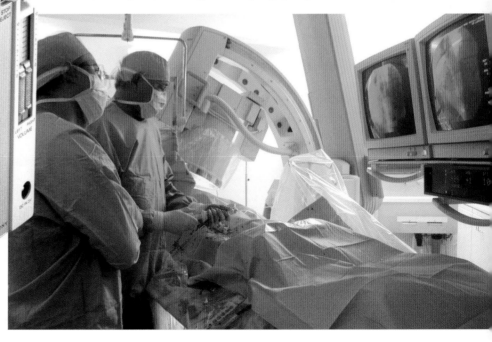

1977-8

EVENTS

• Peace talks arranged by US President Jimmy Carter lead to Egypt and Israel signing Camp David Peace Accords (1978)
• The supertanker *Amoco Cadiz* is wrecked off the coast of Brittany causing terrible oil pollution (1978)
• Former Italian prime minister Aldo Moro is kidnapped and murdered by Red Brigade terrorists (1978)

INVENTIONS

• The Konica C35AF is launched, the first camera with an autofocus function

• German surgeon Andreas Gruentzig undertakes the first coronary angioplasty operation

• American computer programmer Ray Kurzweil unveils his print-to-speech reading machine for the blind

• Inception of the Argos system, the first satellite-based GPS (global positioning system)

• The world's first test-tube baby, Louise Brown, is born in the UK

• French engineer Paul Lipschutz invents a keyless remote central locking device for vehicles

• The use of CFCs (chlorofluorocarbons) in aerosol sprays is banned in the USA

▶ A Trivial Pursuit board with the team behind the new game

▼ Remote electronic car key fob

1979

• Shah Reza Pahlavi of Iran flees into exile as the Islamic Revolution sweeps the country; Ayatollah Ruhollah Khomeini becomes 'supreme leader' of a theocratic state
• The USSR invades Afghanistan at the request of the pro-Soviet government there, and becomes embroiled in a nine-year conflict

• The Trivial Pursuit board game is invented by the Canadians Scott Abbott and Chris Haney and soon becomes an international phenomenon

• The American ice-hockey-playing Olson brothers develop in-line Rollerblade skates

• Physicists Peter Young and Wallace Sargent present convincing evidence for the existence of black holes

• The electronic giants Sony and Philips jointly develop the compact disc

▲ Compact discs

1980

- Lech Walesa, future leader of the Solidarity trade union movement and eventually Polish president, leads strikes in the Gdansk shipyards
- Start of the eight-year Iran–Iraq War
- Zimbabwe becomes independent after a long guerrilla war against white minority rule; Robert Mugabe is elected its first president
- John Lennon is shot dead in New York

- Invention by Dornier Medical Systems (Germany) of the lithotripter, a device that uses ultrasound waves to break up kidney stones

- Engineer Bill Carlton devises the Cyclops electronic service-line monitoring system for the Wimbledon Tennis Championships

- Minitel, a pioneering computerised telecommunications enquiry system, is launched in France with terminals in offices and homes

1981

- General Wojciech Jaruzelski imposes martial law in Poland and dissolves Solidarity
- Republican Ronald Reagan is elected US president
- Egyptian President Anwar Sadat is murdered by Islamist extremists; Hosni Mubarak is his successor
- Prince Charles marries Lady Diana Spencer

- The 3M company of St Paul, Minnesota, lodges a patent for the Post-it® note

- US inventor PaulMcCready builds a solar-powered aircraft, the *Solar Challenger*

- The first portable computer is created by the American entrepreneur Adam Osborne

- The world's first wind farms appear on the skyline of California

- France introduces the TGV high-speed train from Paris to Lyons

▶ A tennis ball reviewed by Cyclops

▶ French president François Mitterrand on board the first TGV

▼ Journalists with laptop computers

1981 (continued)

- Israel annexes the Golan Heights from Syria; Israeli aircraft bomb Beirut
- AIDS is first identified in the United States
- South African troops invade Angola
- Social Democratic Party forms in the UK

- The US space shuttle *Columbia* successfully completes its maiden flight

- Gerd Binnig and Heinrich Rohrer develop the scanning tunnelling microscope

- Mercedes-Benz offers customers optional airbags on its top-of-the-range cars

- Transdermal patches are introduced as a new method of administering drug doses to patients

- Microsoft's MS–DOS operating system is adopted by IBM for its PC (personal computer)

1982

- A British Task Force ousts Argentinian forces from the Falklands
- Israeli troops invade Lebanon to combat attacks by the Palestine Liberation Organisation (PLO)
- USA and USSR begin talks to limit strategic nuclear arms

- American scientists isolate oncogenes, genes that have the potential to cause cancer

- Japanese companies Sony and JVC introduce the camcorder

- Mathematician Benoît Mandelbrot introduces the concept of fractals

- The world's first stealth plane, the Lockheed-Martin F-117 Nighthawk, enters service with the US Air Force

- CD players are developed by Sony and Philips

- Death of Austrian zoologist and ethologist Karl von Frisch, who conducted pioneering research on sensory perception in honey bees

- Martine Kempf develops voice-recognition software that leads to the Katalavox, a device for operating wheelchairs, and magnifying devices in microsurgery

▶ A Douglas F-4 Phantom interceptor and ground-attack aircraft of the US Air Force

◀ Karl von Frisch studing bees

▲ An airbag in operation

1983

1984

- Mass protests against the presence of Cruise and Pershing nuclear missiles on US air bases in Western Europe, including Greenham Common in the UK
- The German Green Party gains its first seats in the *Bundestag*
- The USSR shoots down a Korean airliner over Russian airspace

- Marketing of the first Swatch®, a stylish, inexpensive watch with fewer components than traditional timepieces

- The first mobile phone, the DynaTAC 6000X, is launched in the USA by Motorola

- The McDonnell-Douglas F/A-18 Hornet, one of a new generation of multi-role combat aircraft, enters service

- Apple's Lisa computer introduces the computer mouse and pull-down menus

- Prime Minister Indira Gandhi of India is murdered by extremists among her Sikh bodyguard
- A leak of poisonous gas at the US-owned Union Carbide factory in Bhopal, India, kills more than 2,000 people
- The Sandinistas win national elections in Nicaragua

- Steve Jobs and Apple launch the Macintosh® computer, which becomes the industry standard for designers

- American surgeons pioneer the technique of grafting artificially grown skin to save the lives of two badly burned young boys

- Tobacco plants containing an artificially introduced insecticide spark the long-running debate on the development of genetically modified organisms (GMOs)

- The work of the Japanese researcher Shigeru Chubachi first draws attention to the hole in the ozone layer

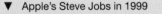

▼ Apple's Steve Jobs in 1999

▼ The Motorola DynaTAC 6000X

▲ Bill Gates in 1998

◄ A Swatch® model from 1983

1985

EVENTS

- Mikhail Gorbachev becomes leader of the USSR; his policies of *glasnost* and *perestroika* lead to the lifting of the Iron Curtain and the fall of the Berlin Wall in 1989–90
- Mass anti-apartheid protests in South Africa lead to the declaration of a state of emergency by the government
- Britain agrees to return Hong Kong to China by 1997

INVENTIONS

- The PET scanner, a medical nuclear imaging device, proves its worth in cardiology, neurology and diagnosis of cancer
- Bill Gates and Microsoft introduce the Windows operating system to replace MS-DOS on PCs
- Apple unveils the LaserWriter, a printer designed to work with desktop publishing (DTP) applications
- American biochemist Kary Mullis conceives of the polymerase chain reaction (PCR), a method of multiplying copies of parts of DNA molecules that later proves a key element in genetic fingerprinting
- Nintendo's SuperNES console stimulates a new and highly lucrative market for video games
- Chemists Richard Smalley and Harold Kroto discover fullerenes
- Undersea explorer Robert Ballard uses an ROV (remotely operated vehicle) to locate the wreck of the *Titanic*

1986-7

EVENTS

- US space shuttle *Challenger* explodes shortly after lift-off (1986)
- Catastrophic explosion and fire at the Chernobyl nuclear power plant in the Ukraine (1986)
- The first Palestinian *Intifada* (uprising) against the Israeli occupation of the West Bank and Gaza (1987)
- Black Monday on world stock markets (1987)

INVENTIONS

- The European Airbus A320 is the first commercial aircraft to use a computer-controlled 'fly-by-wire' system
- Japanese firm Nippon Zeon develops a plastic with 'memory' that can be bent into a new shape which it retains at low temperature but revert to its initial form when warmed
- American astronomers provide proof of the theory that stars originate in the collapse of vast cosmic gas and dust clouds
- FM stations in Europe begin using the radio data system (RDS) to transmit digital data
- The Canadian Imax Corporation develops a cinecamera that can film in 3-D
- A worldwide moratorium on commercial whaling begins by international agreement
- Electronic trading begins on the London Stock Exchange
- Digging begins for the Channel Tunnel

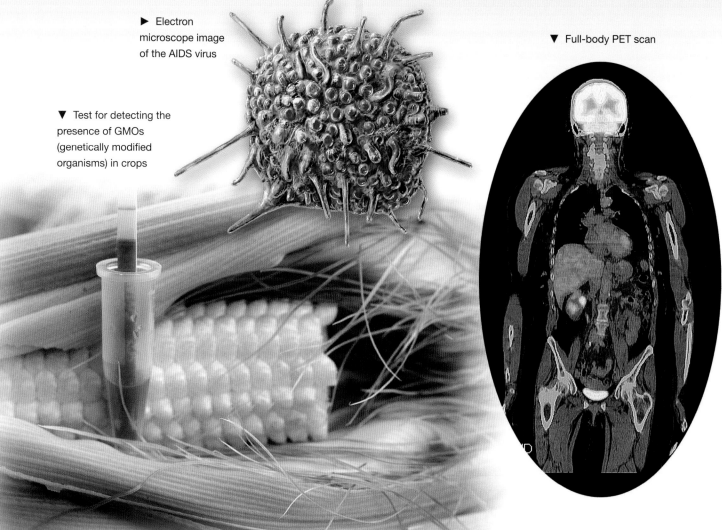

▶ Electron microscope image of the AIDS virus

▼ Test for detecting the presence of GMOs (genetically modified organisms) in crops

▼ Full-body PET scan

1988

- Benazir Bhutto is elected prime minister of Pakistan
- An American Pan-Am jet explodes over Lockerbie in Scotland, killing 270 people; a Libyan agent is later convicted of the attack
- King Hussein of Jordan officially renounces his country's claim on the Israeli-occupied West Bank

- Renowned British physicist Stephen Hawking publishes his account of the origins of the Universe, *A Brief History of Time*

- Representatives of 30 nations meet in Geneva to form the Intergovernmental Panel on Climate Change, studying the role of greenhouse gases in global warming

- Laying of the first transatlantic optical fibre cable

- Cornell graduate Robert Morris develops one of the first computer viruses (the Morris Worm) which spreads around the world affecting 60,000 computers

- The US government decides to fund the sequencing of the human genome (Human Genome Project)

- The first disposable contact lenses go on sale

1989

- Collapse of Communism in Eastern Europe; the Berlin Wall is dismantled; the Velvet Revolution takes place in Czechoslovakia
- Student reform movement in Beijing is crushed by the Chinese Army in Tiananmen Square
- George Bush Snr is sworn in as US President
- Aung San Suu Kyi is placed under house arrest in Burma

- CERN in Geneva introduces the concept of hyperlinks, one of the key steps towards the creation of the Internet

- IBM's *Deep Thought* becomes the first computer to beat a chess grand master

- The GRiDPAD, the first portable microcomputer with touch-screen technology, goes on sale in the USA

- Philips and Sony develop the videodisc

- The world's first conference on nanotechnology is held in Palo Alto, California

- The US Air Force takes delivery of the Northrop Grumman B-2 Spirit; budget cuts reduced a planned order for 132 of this hugely expensive stealth bomber to just 21

▼ Tradition mixes with modernity in Japan

◀ Stephen Hawking

▼ Birth of a stellar black hole

Index

Page numbers in *italics* refer to captions.

A

Abbott, Scott 30
Advanced Mobile Phone Service 107
aeolipile 80
Aeromodeller 80
agribusiness *119*, 123
AGV (*Automotrice à grande vitesse*) 71, *71*
AIDS virus 136-9
airbags 88, *88*
Airbus A300 146
Airbus A320 152
Airbus A380 49
aircraft
  combat aircraft 98-101
  composite materials 49, *49*
  eccentric flying machines *80*, 81
  solar-powered 45, *45*
  stealth aircraft 100, 101, 102-3, *102*, *103*
airport information screens *64*
air traffic control *63*, 65
Aiwa *20*
alarm systems *64*
Aldrin, Buzz *117*
Alfke, Jens *44*
Allen, Bryan *45*
Allen, Paul *56*
all-terrain bikes (ATBs) *147*
Alstom 67, 68
Altair 8800 56, 58
Altamont Pass wind farm 60, *61*
Amazon Basin *128*
American Republic A-10 Thunderbolt 100
Amoco Cadiz 125, 126
analogue signals 62, 111
Anger, Hal 130
angiograms *131*
animal behaviour 94-5
Anschütz-Thoms, Daniela *114*
antibacterial socks 50
antilock braking system (ABS) 146
Antiope 43
antioxidants *121*
Apollo 11 mission 74, 117
Apple 44, 53, 55, 56, 58, 59, 73
Apple II 58, *58*
Apps, Geoff 147
Area 51 101, 102

B

BAe Sea Harrier 98
Baird, John Logie 104
Ballard, Robert 152
Ballmer, Steve 57
ballooning 117
Bardeen, John 110
Barré-Sinoussi, Françoise 136, 138
Baxter, Glen 82
bee behaviour 94-5
Bell, Alexander Graham 110
Bell Labs 107
Bernard, Alain *115*
Betamax 38, 64, 91, 92
Betamovie BMC–100P 91, *91*
Bethesda National Cancer Institute 138
Betrisey, Marcel *85*
Bevan, Michael 119
Bhopal chemical plant 126, *126*
bicycles
  all-terrain bikes (ATBs) 147
  lenticular wheels 115
Big Bang 36, 37
Bill and Melinda Gates Foundation 57
Binnig, Gerd 86, *86*
biocompatible materials 47
bioenginering 120
Birge, Edward 126

Argos system 25, *25*
Armstrong, Neil 117
arrival/departure screens *64*
art and invention 80-5
artificial skin 112, *112*
assisted reproductive technology 26-7
astrophysics 32-7
AT&T Paradyne 64
athletics 114-15, *115*
Atlantis space shuttle 76, 79
atomic bombs 125
atomic force microscopes (AFMs) 86-7
audio books 21
audio cassettes 20, 21
autofocus cameras 22-3, *22*, 141
automatic fuel injection 64
avionics 101
Ayres, William Orville 81
AZT 139

Bishop, Michael 89
black holes 32-5, *34*, *35*, *36*, *37*
Blades, Herbert 50
Bluebird 116, *116*
Blue Riband 116
Boardman, Chris 116
body armour 50
Boeing 787 Dreamliner *49*
Boeing B-29 Superfortress 98
Boeing B-47 Stratojet 98
Boeing B-52 Stratofortress 98, 99
Bold Molding Compound (BMC) *48*
Bolt, Usain 114, *115*
Borg, Björn 46
Borlaug, Norman 122
Borschberg, André 45
Bosch 146
Brattain, Walter 62, 110
Braun, Armin 119
Brendel, Walter 42
Brinster, Ralph 120
British Antarctic Survey 129
Brown, Louise 26, *26*
Brundtland, Gro Harlem 128
buckminsterfullerene 46
buckyballs 46
building materials 49, 50, *50*
bullet-proof vests 50
bullet trains 66-7, *67*
Buran space shuttle 76, *76*
Burke, John 112

C

Calder, Alexander *81*, 82
camcorders 63, 90-3, *90*, *91*, *92*, *93*
cameras 22-3
camouflage-wear 50, *51*
Campbell, Donald 116
Campbell, Malcolm 116
cancer research 89
Canon 72, 73, 141, 142
capsule hotels *140*
carbon fibre 47, 48
carbon footprints 114
car bumpers 48
Carelman, Jacques 82, *82*
Carlton, Bill 42
carotenoids *121*
cars
  airbags 88, *88*
  antilock braking system (ABS) 146
  automatic fuel injection 64
  carphones 107, *107*
  catalytic converters 147
  composite materials 48, *48*
  electronic key fobs 30, 64

  electronics 64
  fantastical cars 84, 85
  nuclear-powered cars 80
  racing cars 49
Carson, Rachel 124
cash machines 65
catalytic converters 147
catamarans *116*, 117
Cavitron 42
CD-100 Magnavox *38*
CDs (compact discs) 38-41, *40*, *41*
  CD burners 40
  CD players 21, *38*, 39
  CD-ROMs 40, *41*, 52
  recordable CDs (CD-R) 40
  rewritable CDs (CD-RW) 40
cellphone networks 108-9
cellphones *see* mobile phones
cement 50
Centronics 101 72
ceramic tiles 46, 47, 75, *75*
Challenger space shuttle 75, 76, 77, *77*
Chandrasekhar, Subrahmanyan 34
Chandrasekhar Limit 34
Chandra X-ray telescope 32
Chang, Min 26
Channel Tunnel 70, 152
chaos theory 97, 146
character and speech recognition 28-9, *28*, *29*
charge-coupled device (CCD) spectrometer 32
Charrier, Bertrand 105
Chaussy, Christian 42
Chermann, Jean-Claude 136
Chernobyl 126
Chilton, Mary-Dell 119
Chitty Chitty Bang Bang 84, 85
chlorofluorocarbons (CFCs) 128, 129
Chubachi, Shigeru 129
Cielo, César *115*
circuit boards 62
climate change 128, 153
Club of Rome 124
cockpit voice control 28-9, 101
Cohen, Stanley 120
Collins, Michael 117
colour printers 73, *73*
Columbia space shuttle 46, 74, *74*, *75*, 76, 79, *79*
Commodore SX-64 Portable 53
communications, global 113-14
Compaq 52
Compaq SLT/286 52
composite materials 47-8, *47*, 51

computer chess 153
computer-controlled
        manufacturing 64
computer mouse 53, 151
computers 52-9
    Apple and Microsoft 56-9
    portable 52-5, *52, 53*
    printers 72-3, *72*
    viruses *59*, 153
Concorde 117, *117*
contact lenses 153
contraceptive patches *88*
Convair B-58 Hustler 99
Convair F-102 Delta Dagger
        99
Convair F-106 Delta Dart 99
Cooper, Geoffrey 89
Cooper, Jacques 66
Cooper, Martin 106, 107
Corian® 49
Cormack, Allan 146
coronarography 131-2
coronary angioplasty 24, *24*
cosmetics industry 112
cosmology 36, 37
Cospas-Sarsat 25
Cousteau, Jacques-Yves 105
Cowles, Henry 126
crease-resistant fabrics 50
Crippen, Robert 74, *74*
Crutzen, Paul 129
CT scanning 64, 132, *132,*
        146
Curl, Robert 46
cycling 115-16, *115*
Cyclops system 42
Cygnus X-1 34

D
Dada 81
Dal Monte, Antonio 115
Dalton, Grant 117
Dassault Mirage III 99
Dassault Rafale 101, *101*
data compression 64
DAT (Digital Audio Tape) 21
DDT 124
deep ecology 126
Deep Thought 153
deforestation *128*
dentistry *42*
desktop publishing (DTP) 58
Dictaphones 21
digital camcorders 93
digital cameras 22, 23, *23,*
        93, 142
digital clocks 62
digital mammography 132
digital signals 62, 111
digital watches 63
Digitizing Line 28
Dire Straits *38, 39*
Discman 21, 39

Discovery space shuttle 76, 78
disposable cameras 141
disposable watches 104
DNA *87, 89, 89,* 118, 139
    manipulation 119, 120, 121
Doi, Toshitada 38
Doppler effect 25
Dotter, Charles 24
Dreyfus-Graf, Jean 28
Duchamp, Marcel 81
DuPont™ *47,* 50
DynaTAC 106, 107

E
Earth Day *125*
Earth Summits 128
eccentric gadgetry 85
Eckart, Andreas *34*
E. coli 120
ecological disasters 125-6
ecological movement 124-8
Edison, Thomas Alva 80
Edwards, Robert 26
Eigler, Donald 87
Einstein, Albert 32, 34, 80
electrocardiograph (ECG) 64
electroencephalogram (EEG)
        64
electronic key fobs 30, 64
electronics 62-5, 143
    see also computers
electronic trading *64, 65,* 152
electronic voting *65*
Emmett, Rowland 85
endangered species 127
Endeavour space shuttle 76, 78
endorphins 147
endoscopy 130-1, *131*
English Electric Lightning 99
ENIAC computer 62
Enterprise space shuttle 75-6
environmentalism 124-8
Epson 52, 72
ergonomics 115
Ericsson 107
Escher, M C 82, 83
E-Ship 1 105
Euro Carex 71
Eurofighter Typhoon 29, 100,
        101
European Food Safety
        Authority (EFSA) 122
Eurostar 70
event horizons 33, 34
Exner, Sigmund 94

F
fantastical inventions 80-5
Farman, Joe 129
Fernandez, Bill 59
Fessenden, Reginald Aubrey
        111

fibreglass 47
fibrinolysis 24
Flavell, Richard 119
Flavr Savr tomatoes 120, *120*
Fleming, John Ambrose 62
Fletcher, James 75
Flettner, Anton 105
Flexon® 48
flight simulators 63
fly-by-wire 101, 152
'Flying Bedstead' 81
Ford Motor Company 80
Forel, François-Alphonse 126
Forssmann, Werner 24
fractal analysis 97
fractal patterns 96-7, *96, 97*
France Telecom 43
Franquin 84
freight transport 71, 114
Frisch, Karl von 94-5, *94*
Fry, Art 44, *44*
Fuji 141
Fujifilm 92
fullerenes 46
functional MRI (fMRI) 130,
        133

G
'Gaffophone' 84
Gagarin, Yuri 74
Gallo, Robert 137, 138
games consoles 152
gamma camera 130
Gardiner, Brian 129
gas-turbine locomotives 67-8
Gates, Bill 56-7, *56, 57*
Gavilan SC 53
General Dynamics F-111 101
General Electric 92
General Motors 147
gene stacking *120*
gene therapy 87, 139
genetically modified organisms
        (GMOs) 118-23
Gerber, Christoph 86
glass fibre 51
Global System for Mobile
        Communications (GSM)
        108
'global village' 114
Gore-Tex® 50, *51*
Gossamer Condor 45
Grand Erg Occidental *96*
graphical user interfaces 53, 58
gravitational collapse 33, 34
gravitational singularities 32,
        33, 34, 36
Green, Andy *116*
greenhouse gases 153
Green movement 124-8
Greenpeace *121, 123,* 126
Green Revolution 122

GriD Compass 1101 52, *52*
GriDPAD 153
growth hormone 120
Gruentzig, Andreas 24
GSM system 109
Gusmão, Bartolomeu de 81

H
Haeckel, Ernst 126
haemoglobin *119*
Haise, Fred 76
Handycam *93*
Haney, Chris 30
Haney, John 30
Hary, Armin 114
Hausdorff, Felix 97
'Have Blue' aircraft prototype
        102-3
Hawk-eye system 42
Hawking, Stephen 36-7, *36, 37*
Hawking radiation 36
Hayek, Nicolas 104
head-up displays 101
Heath Robinson, William 81
Helios 45, *45*
herbicides 120, 121
Hero of Alexandria 80
Herrick, John W 88
Hewlett-Packard 63, 72-3
high-speed train (HST)
        programmes 66-71
Hiroshima 125
Hitachi 93
HIV infection 136-9
Hogarth, William 82
Honda 142-3
Honda, Soichiro 142-3
house-building technology
        49-50, *49*
HTLV-1 virus 137
HTLV-2 virus 138
HTLV-3 virus 138
Hubble Space Telescope 78, *78*
Hudson, Rock 138
Hughes, John 147
Hulse, Russell A 147
Human Genome Project 153
Hunkin, Tim 85
Hunter, Max 75
hydrofoil yachts 116-17
hyperlinks 153
Hypersonic Experimental
        Vehicle *117*

I
IBM 52, 57, 72
IBM 3800 73
iBook *58*
iMac *58*
Imax Corporation 152
Immink, Kees Schouhamer 38
information technology 63

infrared sensors 64
inkjet printers 72, 73
Inktronic 72
in-line skating 31
Inmarsat (INternational MARitime SATellite Organization) 108
insulin 120
integrated circuits 110
Intel 4004 processor 62, 110
Intel 8008 processor 63
Intergovernmental Panel on Climate Change 153
International Space Station (ISS) 79
International Union for the Conservation of Nature (IUCN) 127
Internet 21, 40, 41, 153
Internet Protocol (IP) 111
intracytoplasmic sperm injection (ICSI) 27, *27*
intrauterine insemination 27
in vitro fertilization (IVF) 26-7
iPad 58, *59*
iPhone 58
iPod 21, 40, 58
Ishitawa, Shigetane 118

J

James Bond films 75, 84
Japanese work culture 140-1, *142*
Jarvik, Murray 88
Jobs, Steve 56, 57-8, *57*, *58*, *59*
Johnston, Harold 129
Jones, Brian 117
joysticks 53
Jungner, Waldemar 110
Juul, Johannes 60
JVC 64, 91, 92, 93

K

Kaposi's sarcoma 136
karoshi 140
Katalavox 29
Kawakami, Kenji 85, *85*
Kawasaki 143
Kempf, Martine 29
Kerr, Roy 34
Kevlar® 47, 50
keyhole surgery 131
Kinetoscope 80
Kodak 90, 91
Kodak Zoom 8 *90*
KodaVision 2000 91
Konica C35AF 22
Kops, Jesse 44
Kosterlitz, Hans 147

Kroto, Harold 46
Kurokawa, Kisho 142
Kurzweil, Ray 28, *28*
Kwolek, Stephanie 50
Kyoto Agreement *126*

L

Landfill Prize 85
Landsat 1 146
land-speed records 116
laparoscopy 26
laptops 52-5
Laserjet 72
laser printers 72-3
LaserWriter 73
Lauterbur, Paul 146
Leibovitch, Jacques 136
lenticular wheels 115
Leonardo da Vinci 80
Lipschutz, Paul 30
liquid-crystal display (LCD) 54
lithium-ion batteries 46, *54*, 110
lithium-polymer batteries 110
lithotripsy 42
Lockheed A-12 Oxcart 102
Lockheed F-22 Raptor 103, *103*
Lockheed F-104 Starfighter 99
Lockheed F-117 Nighthawk 102, *102*
Lockheed SR-71 Blackbird 99, *103*, 117
Lockheed YO-3A Quiet Star 103
Longo, Jeannie 115
Lorenz, Edward 146
Lucas, Caroline 124
Lucy (early hominid) 147
lymphadenopathy 136-7
Lynas, Mark 128

M

M87 galaxy 32, *32*, 34
McAuliffe, Christa 77, *77*
MacBook Air 55, *55*
MacCready, Paul 45
McDonnell Douglas F-4 Phantom 98, 99, 101
McDonnell Douglas F-15 Eagle 101, 103
McDonnell Douglas F/A-18 Hornet 98, *100*
Mach, Ernst 100
Mach numbers 100
Macintosh 58
McLuhan, Marshall 114
Maglev trains 67, 113
magnetic resonance imaging (MRI) 64, 132, 133, *133*, 134, *134*

magnetic resonance spectroscopy (MRS) 64
magnetostrictive materials 48
Magnus, Heinrich Gustav 105
Magnus Effect 105
Malavard, Lucien 105
Mallard 67
Mandelbrot, Benoît 96, 97
Marconi, Guglielmo 111
Mars missions 79
Marti, Bernard 43
materials, new 46-51
Meadows, Dennis 124
medical imaging 64, 130-5, 142
  angiograms *131*
  coronarography 131-2
  CT scanning 64, 132, *132*, 146
  digital mammography 132
  endoscopy 130-1, *131*
  functional MRI (fMRI) 130, 133
  MRI scanning 64, 132, 133, *133*, 134, *134*
  MRS (magnetic resonance spectroscopy) 64
  neurosurgery 134
  PET (positron emission tomography) scanning 135, *135*
  scintigraphy 130, *130*
  videocapsules *130*, 131
medically assisted procreation (MAP) 27
medicine
  AIDS virus 136-9
  artificial skin 112, *112*
  assisted reproductive technology 26-7
  coronary angioplasty 24, *24*
  electrocardiograph (ECG) 64
  electroencephalogram (EEG) 64
  fibrinolysis 24
  implants and prostheses 47
  laparoscopy 26
  lithotripsy 42
  medical imaging 64, 130-5, 142
  oncogenics 89
  renal ultrasound 42, *42*
  tissue repair 47
  transdermal delivery system 88, *88*
Meier, Richard *50*
Mercedes-Benz 88
Merckx, Eddy 115
mercury poisoning 125
metamaterials 51
Micral-N 63
Micro Instrumentation and Telemetry Systems (MITS) 56

micrometric technology 51
microprocessors 62, 110
Microsoft *56-7*, 59, 63
MicroTAC 8900X *107*
MiG-19 98
MiG-21 99
MiG-25 100
military aircraft 98-103
Milky Way 34
miniaturisation 22
MiniDisc 21
MiniDV (Digital Video) cassettes 93
Minitel 43, *43*
Minolta Maxxum 7000 22
Mitchell, John F 106, *106*, 107
mobile phones 106-11, 113
Möbius strip 82
Moggridge, Bill 52
Molina, Mario 129
Monsanto 119, 120, *120*
Montagnier, Luc 136, 138
Montreal Protocol 129
Moon exploration 79, 117
Moore, Frank *136*
Moore, Gordon 62
Moreno, Roland 147
Morita, Akio 20, 21, 143
Morris, Robert 153
Morrow, John 120
Morse code 111
Moser, Francesco 115
motorbikes 143
Motorola 106, 108, 110
motor racing 113
MP3 players 21, 40
MRI scanning 64, 132, 133, *133*, 134, *134*
MS/DOS 57
Mullis, Kary 152
music
  CDs (compact discs) 38-41, *38*, *40*, *41*
  personal stereos 20-1, *20*
music piracy 41

N

Nagasaki 125
Naish, John 85
nanometric technology 51
nanoparticles 51
nanotechnology 87
nanotubes 46
Napster 41
NASA 25, 45, 60, 74-9, 146
Nasworthy, Frank 146
NEC 52
Nester, Eugene 119
networking sites 113-14
neurosurgery 134
neutron stars 34
NeXT Computer 58

NGC 6240 galaxy *33*, 34
nickel-cadmium batteries 110
nickel-cadmium cells 54
nicotine patches 88
Nieh, James 95
Niepce brothers 80
Nikon 141
Nikon F3AF 22, *22*
Nintendo 152
Nippon Zeon 152
Nixon, Richard 74
Nokia 108
Nomex® *47*
Northrop B-2 Spirit 103
notebooks 54, 55
Noyle, Robert 110

O

oil crisis 125
oil spills 125, *125*
Olson, Scott 31
Olympus 142
oncogenics 89
Oppenheimer, Robert 34
optical character recognition (OCR) 28
organic light-emitting diodes (OLEDs) 55
Osborne, Adam 52, *52*
Osborne 1 portable computer 52
ozone layer 128, 129, *129*

P

pachinko machines *143*
Palermo, Gianpiero 27
Palmiter, Richard 120
Panamarenko *80*, 81
Panasonic 92, 93
Panavia Tornado 100
parallax phenomenon 22
Pasteur Institute 138
Pavel, Andreas 20, 21
Pawlowski, Gaston de 80, 81
Penrose, Lionel 83
Penrose, Roger 36
Penrose Stairs 83
Pentax ME-F 22
personal stereos 20-1, *20*
pesticides 124
PET (positron emission tomography) scanning 135, *135*
Philips 20, 38, 39, 40, 92
phonetograph 28
photography
  autofocus cameras 22-3, *22*, 141
  camcorders 63, 90-3, *90*, *91*, *92*, *93*

digital cameras 22, 23, *23*, 142
disposable cameras 141
webcams 55
phtalocyanine *86*
Piccard, Auguste 45
Piccard, Bertrand 45, 117
piezoelectric materials 48
pilotless drones *45*, 99
Pincus, Gregory 26
pinpoint strategic bombing 98
Pixar Studios 58
plant development, transgenic 119-23
pocket calculators 63
Polaroid 22, 92
pollution *124*, 125, *126*, *127*
pollution-resistant concrete 50, *50*
polycarbonate 49
polymerase chain reaction (PCR) 152
Portapak 90-1
Post-it® notes 44, *44*
Post-it® Software Notes 44
PowerBook 500 53
Powers, Gary 99
primordial black holes 34
printer technology 72-3, *72*
Proffit, Franck 117
Project Gutenberg 28
prostheses 47
pulsar 147
Pulsar (watch) 63
pyréolophore 80

Q

Q0906+6930 black hole 34
quantum mechanics 36, 37
Quate, Calvin 86

R

radar 101, 102
radiation 129, *129*, 130
  Hawking radiation 36
radio data system (RDS) 152
radioisotopes 130
radiotelephones 107, *107*, 110
Raetz, Markus 82, *83*
rail travel 66-71
Rainbow Warrior 126
Ramsar Convention 127
rangefinders 23, *23*
reconnaissance aircraft 99
recycling 51, 73
Red List 127
relativity theory 32, 33-4, 36
Remensnyder, John 112
remotely operated vehicles (ROVs) 152

renal ultrasound 42, *42*
Renault Espace 48
retro-reflectum *51*
retroviruses 136, 137
Reutersvärd, Oscar 82
Rifkin, Jeremy 122
RNA *89*, 136, 139
Roberts, Ed 56
Rochon, Alexis Marie 23
Rocket 67
Rohrer, Heinrich 86, *86*
rollerblades 31, *31*
roller hockey 31
rolling news broadcasting 114
Romanesco broccoli *96*
Rose, Jed 88
Roundup 120
Rowland, Frank Sherwood 129
Rozenbaum, Willy 136
Rubik, Erno 147
Rubik Cube 147
Rushka, Ernst 86

S

Sagittarius A black hole 34, *34*
sailing 116-17, *116*
St Clair Kilby, Jack 110
Salomon, Albert 132
Sargent, Wallace 32
satellite phones 108
satellites
  Argos system 25, *25*
  Cospas-Sarsat 25
  Helios 45
  Landsat 1 146
SatNav 29
Saturn V rockets 74
scanning electron microscopes (SEMs) 86
scanning tunnelling microscopes (STMs) 86-7, *86*, *87*
Schell, Jeff 119
Schmiedt, Egbert 42
Schwarzschild, Karl 33-4
scintigraphy 130, *130*
Sculley, John 58
search-and-rescue network 25
self-repairing materials 48
semiconductors 64
SentryGlass® *49*
Shanklin, Jon 129
Shannon, Claude 111
shape-memory alloys (SMA) 48, *48*
Sharp 93
Shelley, Mary 84
Shepard, David 28
Shinkansen 66-7, *67*
Shockley, William 110
side-entry bathtub 80

Silent Spring 124
Silver, Spencer 44
SIM cards 107, 110
Sinclair, Sir Clive 80
Sinclair C5 80
Sinclair ZX Spectrum 21
sintering 47
skateboarding 146
Skylab 146
Smalley, Richard 46
smart cards 147
smartphones 109, *111*
smogs 125, *126*
Snyder, Hartland 34
Solar Challenger 45, *45*
Solar Impulse 45
solar-powered aircraft 45, *45*
Solovyov, Igor 104
Solovyoya, Maria 104
somatostatin 120
Son, Masayoshi 142
Sony 20-1, 38, 39, 40, 64, 90, 91, 92, 93, 110, 143
Sosenka, Ondrej 115
space shuttles 46, 47, 74-9, *74*, *75*, *76*, *77*, *79*
  Russian 76, *76*
spacetime 33, 34, 35
spectacle frames *48*
speech recognition programs 28-9, *29*
speed 113-17
speedboats 49
speed governors 64
speed skating *114*
Starkweather, Gary 72
stealth aircraft 100, 101, 102-3, *102*, *103*
stealth military equipment 51
steel 47
Stehelin, Dominique 89
stellar black holes *32*, 33, 34
stem cells 112, *112*
stents 24, *24*
Stephenson, George 67
Steptoe, Patrick 26
stereobelt 20, 21
Stickies 44
Stockholm Declaration 128
stock markets *64*, *65*
strategic bombers 98-9
Sukhoi Su-9 99
Sukhoi Su-15 99
Super 8 movie film 90
Super Audio CDs 39
surface-to-air missiles 99
Surrealism 81, 82
sustainable development 128
Suzuki 143
S-VHS format 92
Swatch® 104, *104*
Swift, Jonathan 83-4
swimming *115*

SX-70 camera 22
synthetic fibres 50
System Identification Code
    (SID) 106

T
Tabary, Francis *83*
Tablet PC 54
Tachi, Susumu *51*
'Tacit Blue' aircraft prototype
    102
Tange, Kenzo 142
Taylor, Joseph H 147
T-DNA 119
Teflon 50
Teldix GmbH 146
telephones
    early telephones 110-11
    mobile phones 106-11, 113
    satellite phones 108
teleprinters 72
television
    3-D television 104, *104*
    colour television 143
tennis line calls 42
tennis raquets 46
test-tube babies 26-7
Texas Instruments 63
text messaging 108, *109*
TGV (*Train à grande vitesse*)
    66-9, *66*, *67*, 117
Thébault, Alain 117
thermal printers 72
thermionic valves 62
thermoelectric materials 48
thermoplastic resins *48*
Thomke, Ernst 104
Thorne, Kip 34
3-D television 104, *104*
3M Corporation 44
Three Mile Island nuclear
    reactor 126
time dilation 33
Timeflex watch 104
time travel 84, 85
Tinguely, Jean 81-2, *81*
tissue repair 47
Titanic 152
Tokyo 140-3
Toshiba 20
Toshiba T1100 *52*
touchpads 53
touch-screen technology 153
Toy Story 58

trains 66-71
transatlantic optical fibre
    cables 153
transdermal patches 88, *88*
transgenesis 118-21
transistor radios 143
transistors 62, 110
Trivial Pursuit 30, *30*
tungsten-carbide 47
Tupolev Tu-16 98
Tupolev Tu-22M 99
Tupolev Tu-95 98
Tupolev Tu-144 Concordski
    117
Tupolev Tu-160 Blackjack 100,
    100
turbosails 105, *105*
turbotrains 67-8

U
Uchida, Shozo 142
UN Conference on the Human
    Environment 127-8
Uniprinter 72
USB ports 55

V
vacuum tubes 62
Van der Waals' forces 86-7
Van Montagu, Marc 119
Varmus, Harold 89
Vaughan, Norman *108*
VHS format 64
videocapsules *130*, 131
video-conferencing 55
video editing 93
video games 63
video players 63
videotex service 43
vinyl LPs 39
virtual notes 44
virtual retinal display (VRD)
    glasses *104*
voice recognition systems 29
Volvo 88
Vought F-8 Crusader *98*

W
Walkman® 20, *20*, *21*, 143
Warming, Eugenius 126
washing machines 63

watches
    digital watches 63
    disposable watches 104
    Swatch® 104, *104*
Watt, James 80
Wayne, Ronald 58
webcams 55
weightlessness *36*, 77
Weinburg, Robert 89
Wells, H G 84
Werner, Ed 30
whaling 152
Wheatstone, Sir Charles 104
Wheeler, John 34
white holes 35
WiFi 55
Wigler, Michael 89
wind farms 60-1, *61*
Windows 54, 57, 59, *59*
windsurfing *113*
wind turbines 60-1, *60*
wireless telegraphy 111
Wonder, Stevie 28
worm holes 35
Wozniak, Steve 56, 57-8, *57*,
    59

X
XB-70 Valkyrie 99
Xerox 72
X-ray treatment 131-2

Y
Yannas, Ioannis 112
Young, John 74, *74*
Young, Peter 32
Young, Russell 86

Z
Zaenen, Ivo 119
Zemeckis, Robert 85
Zwicky, Fritz 34

Picture credits

ABBREVIATIONS: t = top, c = centre, b = bottom, l = left, r = right

Front cover: main image: 1980s traders using mobile phones, Getty Images/Jonathan Kirn; inset: a Walkman TPS-L2 © Sony France.
Spine: The human brain © Cosmos/SPL/Zephyr.
Back cover: Northrop B-2 Spirit Stealth bomber, Corbis/Aero Graphics, Inc.
Page 2, left to right, top row: © Sony France; Corbis/Bettmann; © Nikon; 2nd row: © Nordica; Cosmos/Zephyr/SPL; France Telecom; 3rd row: Sipa Press/ANP Photo/Ben Hansen; © Mini-cubes Post-It® 3M; © with the kind permission of DuPontTM; bottom row: Cosmos/Tony McConnell; Cosmos/Science Museum, London; © Cosmos/SPL/Zephyr.

Pages 4-5: Getty Images/The Image Bank/Tom Bonaventure; 6t: © Nikon; 6bl: Rue des Archives/BCA/'Pretty Woman', directed by Garry Marshal, with Julia Roberts, Buena Vista Pictures, 1990; 6br: © CLS; 6/7t: Gamma-Rapho/Keystone-France; 7t: Cosmos/SPL/Mehau Kulyk; 7b: © Nordica; 8t: RÉA/Hanning/ Nasa; 8bl: Sipa Press/ANP Photo/Ben Hansen; 8br: France Telecom; 9tl: AFP/Dominique Faget; 9tr: © Mini-cubes Post-It® 3M; 9b: © Gore-Tex®; 10tl: Cosmos/Science & Society; 10bl: Corbis/EPA/Herwig Vergult; 10/11t: Corbis/Bob Sacha; 11t: Corbis/Roger Ressmeyer; 11cr: SNCF Médiathèque/Christian Delemarre; 11bl: Signatures/Philippe Schuller; 11t: Cosmos/Science Museum, London; 12b: © Francis Tabary, the Penrose Triangle; 12/13t: Sucré Salé; 13t: Cosmos/SPL/Department of Energy; 13cd: CNRS Photothèque/Stehelin D. Vandenbunder, Unité d'oncologie moléculaire, Lille, France; 13b: © with the kind permission of Sony; 14tl: Corbis/Aero Graphics, Inc.; 14tr: Corbis/George Steinmetz; 14bl: © The Cousteau Society; 14/15b: AFP/Adrian Dennis; 15tl: Cosmos/SPL/Mauro Fermariello; 15tr: © with the kind permission of Nokia; 16l: RÉA/The New York Times/Monsanto; 16t: Reuters/Fatih Saribas; 16tr: Cosmos/SPL/Goddard Space Center; 16/17b: Getty Images/The Image Bank/Tom Bonaventure; 17tl: Cosmos/SPL/Simon Fraser; 17tr: Gamma-Rapho/Rapho/Jean-Claude Coutausse; 18/19: Corbis/Itar-Tass/Vasily Smimov; 20tr: © Sony France; 20b: Sipa Press/AP/Neal Ulevich; 21t: Rue des Archives/BCA/'Pretty Woman', directed by Garry Marshal, with Julia Roberts, Buena Vista Pictures, 1990; 21b: Sipa Press/Lehtikuva Oy/Matti; 22t: © Nikon; 22b: RÉA/Michel Gaillard; 23t: Cosmos/SPL/Joe Pasienka; 23b: Getty Images/Travelpix Ltd; 24l: BSIP/Laurent; 24r: ISM/Sovereign; 25t: © CNES/CL ArtPresse, 2002; 25bl: © CLS/Photon-Ovalie; 25br: © CLS; 26/27t: Gamma-Rapho/Keystone-France; 26c: Getty Images/Hulton Archives; 27t: Corbis/Kipa/Patrick Guis; 27b: Cosmos/Zephyr/SPL; 28t: Corbis/Bettmann; 28b: RÉA/Denis; 29t: Cosmos/SPL/Mehau Kulyk; 29c: RÉA/Denis; 30t: Getty Images/Chemistry; 30bl: Getty Images/Time & Life Pictures/Arthur Schatz; 30br: © Trivial Pursuit TM; 31t: © Nordica; 31b: Getty Images/Eduardo Garcia; 32t: Cosmos/SPL/NASA; 33t: RÉA/Hanning/NASA; 33cr: © NASA/with the kind permission of Nasaimages.org; 34bl: Corbis/Science Faction/ Peter Ginker; 34br: Cosmos/SPL/NSF/AUI/NRAO; 35b: Cosmos/SPL/ESA; 36: AFP; 36/37t: NASA/E/PO, Sonoma State University, Aurore Simonnet; 37cl: Corbis/EPA/Salvatore Di Nolfi; 38/39t: RÉA/Pascal Sittler; 38t: Corbis/Kipa/Catherine Cabrol; 38b: Sipa Press/ANP Photo/Ben Hansen; 40b: Look at Sciences/John Millar; 41t: Corbis/Westend61/Franck Muckenheim; 41cr: Getty Images/Dorling Kindersley; 41b: ANA/David Ducoin; 42tl: Getty Images/Photonica/Gregor Schuster; 42tr: Getty Images/Hulton Archives/Franck Tewkesbury; 42b: BSIP/Southern Illinois University; 43t: France Telecom; 43c: Roger Viollet/Carlos Gayoso; 43b: Sipa Press/Collection Ribière; 44t: © Mini-cubes Post-It® 3M; 44cr: © Index Post-It® 3M; 44bl: © Art Fry 3M; 45t: © NASA/with the kind permission of Nasaimages.org, Photo PMRF/Nick Galante; 45b: AFP/Dominique Faget; 46/47t: BSIP/James L. Amos; 46b: Cosmos/SPL/Victor Habbick Visions; 47t: © with the kind permission of DuPont TM; 47b: Look at Sciences/Patrick Dumas; 48/49t: RÉA/The New York Times/Nicole Bengiveno; 48c: Doublevue.fr/Pascal Goetgheluck; 48b: © PSA Peugeot Citrëon/Direction de la Communication/Photo: Miguel Tillous; 49br, 49b, 50t: © with the kind permission of DuPontTM; 50b: Artedia/View/Edmund Sumner, Architect: Richard Meier and Partners, 2003; 51t: AFP/Yoshikatsu Tsuno; 51b: © Gore-Tex®; 52t: Corbis/Bettmann; 52b: Cosmos/Science & Society; 53t Getty Images/Tim Graham; 53b: Corbis/DPA/A3464 Rainer Jensen; 54: Corbis/Yi Lu; 55t: RÉA/Nicolas Tavernier; 55b: © with the kind permission of Apple; 56t: Getty Images/Joe McNally; 56/57b: AFP/Getty Images/Ryan Anson; 57t: Getty Images/Jeff Christensen; 57cr: AFP/ Getty Images/Jimin Lai; 58t: RÉA/Tom Craig; 58l: Getty Images/Time Life Pictures/Ted Thai; 58tr: Corbis/Roger Ressmeyer; 59tr: © with the kind permission of Apple; 59b: Corbis/Frédéric Neema; 60tl: RÉA/Zenit-Laif/Paul Langrock; 60b: RÉA/Richard Damoret; 61t: Corbis/Owaki-Kulla; 61cr: Corbis/EPA/Herwig Vergult; 62tr: BSIP/Phototake/Maximilian; 62c: Cosmos/SPL/Paul Wootton; 63t: Corbis/Bob Sacha; 63b: RÉA/Michel Gaillard; 64t AFP/Getty Images North America/Chris Hondros; 64b: RÉA/Gilles Rolle; 65t: RÉA/The New York Times/Barbara P. Fernandez; 65b: RÉA/Panos/Andrew McConnell; 66tr: AFP/Dominique Faget; 66bl: AFP/SNCF; 66b: SNCF, Médiathèque/Christian Delemarre; 67: AFP/Getty Images/Tsuno Yoshikazu; 68t: Hemis.FR/Camille Moirenc; 68b: Getty Images/Patrick Landmann; 69t: Gamma-Rapho/Hoa Qui/Michel Troncy; 69b: RÉA/Nicolas Tavernier; 70t: Gamma-Rapho/Gamma/Gregory Gerault; 70b: Urba Images Server/J.F. Fourmond/Architects: Jean-Marie Duthilleul and Jean-François Blassel, 2001, D.R.; 71tl: RÉA/Gilles Rolle; 71tr: AFP/China Xtra; 72: Corbis/Bettmann Film, 'His Other Woman', directed by Walter Lang, with Spencer Tracy and Katharine Hepburn, 20th Century Fox, 1957; 73t: Signatures/Philippe Schuller; 73r: © Canon; 74l, 74c, 75t, 75c: Corbis/Roger Ressmeyer; 76l: Corbis; 76l: AFP/TASS; 77t: AFP/Getty Images/Brian Cleary; 77bl, 77br: Corbis/Bettmann; 78: Corbis/NASA/Roger Ressmeyer; 79t, 79cr: Getty Images/NASA; 79b: Cosmos/SPL/NASA; 80tr: Collection Kharbine Tapabor/Illustration by Adrien Barrère, 1877-1931; 80cl: AKG Images/Brigitte Hellgoth Henry van Herwegen dit Panamarenko, D.R.; 81tr: RMN/Gérard Blot/Bascule M.K.6, Jean Tinguely, 1965 © Adagp, Paris 2011/Musée des Beaux-Arts, Nantes; 81b: Dist.RMN/Jean-Claude Planchet/Alexander Calder, 1929 © Calder Foundation New-York/Adagp, Paris 2011 © RMN/photograper André Kertész © Collection Centre Pompidou, Musée national d'Art moderne, Paris; 82tl, 82tr: © Catalogue of Unfindable Objects, Jacques Carelman, Éditions Le Cherche-Midi, 1997; 82b: © Glen Baxter; 83t: © Francis Tabary, the Penrose Triangle; 83bl: Metamorphosis II, Markus Raetz, 1991-92/Private collection/Photo Thomas Wey © Adagp, Paris 2011, with the kind permission of Galerie Farideh Cadot, Paris; 83br: © UCL Library, London/The Impossible Staircase, Lionel Penrose, 1962; 84t: Collection Christophe L/'The Time Machine', directed by George Pal, with Rod Taylor, 1960; 84b: © Marsu 2010 By Franquin – www.gastonlagaffe.com; 85t: Marcel Betrisey/ Paix des ménages; 85cl: © Catalogue of Unfindable Objects, Jacques Carelman, Éditions Le Cherche-Midi, 1997; 85b: Corbis/EPA/Everett Kennedy Brown; 86t: Look at Sciences/CEMES-CNRS/Patrick Dumas; 86c: Cosmos/SPL/ American Institute of Physics/Emilio Segre Visual Archives; 87t: Cosmos/Science Museum, London; 87b: BSIP/Volker Steger; 87br: Cosmos/SPL/Lawrence Livermore Laboratory; 88t: Getty Images/The Image Bank/Patti McConville; 88b: Cosmos/SPL/Gusto Productions; 89t: CNRS Photothèque/Stehelin D. Vandenbunder, Unité d'oncologie moléculaire, Lille, France; 89b: BSIP/Jim Dowdalls; 90tr: Cosmos/Science Museum, London; 90cl: Corbis/Hulton-Deutsch Collection; 91t: Collection Christophe L/ 'Sex, Lies and Videotape', directed by Steven Soderbergh, with Andie MacDowell, 1989; 91b: © with kind permission of Sony; 92t: RÉA/Benoît Decout; 92b: AGE Fotostock/David H. Wells; 92/93t: Corbis/In visu/Olivier Coret; 93b: © with the kind permission of Sony; 94l: Getty Images/Time and Life Pictures/Nina Leen; 94c: Cosmos/SPL/Bonnier Publications/Lena Untidt; 95t: Cosmos/SPL/James King-Holmes; 95c: Cosmos/SPL/Department of Energy; 96c: Altitude/Yann Arthus-Bertrand; 96b: Sucré Salé; 98: Getty Images/National Geographic/Wilbur E. Garrett; 99t: Corbis/Aero Graphics, Inc.; 99cr: Getty Images/Usaf; 100t: Gamma-Rapho/Gamma/Konstantin Zavrazhin; 100c: Corbis/Itar-Tass/Vasily Smimov; 100b: Cosmos/US Department of Defense; 101t: Alain Ernoult/Ernoult.com; 101c: RÉA/Gilles Rolle; 102t: Corbis/Science Faction/Edwards Air Force Base-Digital; 102b: Corbis/Aero Graphics, Inc.; 103t: Corbis/NASA-Digital Version Copyright; 103c: Getty Images/Joe McNally; 104tr: Corbis/George Steinmetz; 104c: RÉA/Denis; 104b: © Swatch Ltd; 105t: Corbis/Hulton-Deutsch Collection; 105b: © The Cousteau Society; 106t: Leemage/Gusman; 106b: Corbis/Bettmann; 107tl: Getty Images/Chris Ware; 107cr: Cosmos/Tony McConnell; 108t: Getty Images/Jonathan Kirn; 108b: Getty Images/National Geographic/Gordon Wiltsie; 109t: Getty Images/India Today Group/Dilip Banerjee; 109b: RÉA/Pachacamac/Nathan Vreesmarc; 110tr: Leemage/Bianchetti; 110cl: Leemage/Farabola; 110bl & bcl: Jean-Pierre Delagarde; 110bcd: Cosmos/SPL/Cordelia Molloy; 110/111c: © with the kind permission of Nokia; 111tr: RÉA/Reporters/Danny Gys; 111cr: Jean-Pierre Delagarde/Véronique Zonca; 111br: © with the kind permission of Nokia; 112tr: Cosmos/ SPL; 112cl: Cosmos/SPL/Mauro Fermariello; 113tr: Corbis/Abed Al Hashlamoun; 113b: Jérôme Houyvet/Lumieresmarines.com; 114/115t: AFP/Adrian Dennis; 114b: AFP/Getty Images/Bongarts; 115cr: Corbis/Xinhua Press/Fei Maohua; 115b: Corbis/Tim de Waele; 116t: AFP/Marcel Mochet; 116b: Corbis/Hulton-Deutsch Collection; 117t: Cosmos/SPL/NASA; 117b: AFP/Odd Andersen; 119t: RÉA/The New York Times/Monsanto; 119b: RÉA/Laif/Stephan Elleringmann; 120tl: RÉA/Mario Fourmy; 120cr: AFP/Mychèle Daniau; 120b: BSIP/Phototake/Pantages; 121t: Look at Sciences/Massimo Brega; 121b: AFP/Michaël Latz; 122t: AFP/Patrick Herzog; 122c: AFP/Jean-Pierre Muller; 122b: RÉA/Richard Damoret; 123cr: RÉA/AGStock/Scott Sinklier; 123b: RÉA/Hollande Hoogte/Peter Blok; 124t: Corbis/Sygma/Jean-Pierre Laffont; 124c: Reuters/China Daily; 125t: Reuters/Fatih Saribas; 125b: Gamma-Rapho/Gamma/Yves Gladu; 126t: Getty Images/Pablo Bartholomew; 126/127b: AFP/Richard A. Brooks; 127t: AFP/Dimitar Dilkoff; 128t: Corbis/Galen Rowell; 128cr: Cosmos/SPL/ Christian Darkin; 129tr: Cosmos/SPL/Goddard Space Center; 129b: Cosmos/SPL/Michael Gilbert; 130r: BSIP/Cmsp; 130c: BSIP/A. Benoist; 131t: Cosmos/SPL/PHT; 131cr: Cosmos/SPL/Manfred Kage; 131bl: BSIP/Phototake/CNRI; 132t: RÉA/Redux/The New York Times/Andrew Testa; 132cl: BSIP/Phototake/PDSN; 133tr: Cosmos/SPL/Simon Fraser; 133cl: Cosmos/SPL/Zephyr; 134: RÉA/Reporters/Jean-Michel Clajot; 135t: BSIP/H.Raguet; 135b: BSIP/Neil Borden; 136t: Cosmos/SPL/Cristina Pedrazzini; 136c: Cosmos/SPL/Russell Kightley; 137t: Gamma-Rapho/Gamma/Lu Guang; 138t: Corbis/Robert Maass; 138b: www.gregcirade.com; 139t: Gamma-Rapho/Rapho/Jean-Claude Coutausse; 139cr: RÉA/Ropi/Antonio Pisacreta; 140cr: RÉA/The New York Times/Ko Sasaki; 140bl: Corbis/Bettmann; 141t & 141b: Sipa Press/ Ben Simmons; 142t: Hemis.FR/Bruno Perousse; 142c: Getty Images/Stone/Holos; 142/143t: Getty Images/The Image Bank/Tom Bonaventure; 143b: Hemis.FR/Franck Guiziou; 144/145: SNCF Médiathèque/Christian Delemarre; 146l: RÉA/ Redux/The New York Times/Andrew Testa; 146tl: Cosmos/SPL/Zephyr; 146b: RÉA/Michel Gaillard; 147l: © Sony France; 147t: Sipa Press/Lehtikuva Oy/Matti; 147b: BSIP/Laurent; 148tr: Getty Images/Time & Life Pictures/Arthur Schatz; 148b: Getty Images/Chemistry; 148bl: Getty Images/Dorling Kindersley; 149tl: Getty Images/Photonica/Gregor Schuster; 149tr: AFP/Dominique Faget; 149b: Getty Images/Tim Graham; 150t: Getty Images/Usaf; 150bl: Getty Images/Time and Life Pictures/Nina Leen; 150bl: Getty Images/The Image Bank/Patti McConville; 151l: Getty Images/Time Life Pictures/Ted Thai; 151cl: Getty Images/Jeff Christensen; 151r: Cosmos/Tony McConnell; 151b: © Swatch Ltd; 152tl: Cosmos/SPL/Russell Kightley; 152tr: BSIP/Neil Borden; 152b: AFP/Jean-Pierre Muller; 153t: Corbis/EPA/Salvatore Di Nolfi; 153br: Sipa Press/Ben Simmons.

Illustrations on pages 32b, 153bl (birth of a stellar black hole), 35t (supermassive black hole and worm hole), 40t (burning a CD), 96/97t (a fractal), 110br (integrated circuit), 118 (the process of producing a genetically modified organism), 133br (MRI scanner tunnel), 137b (the replication cycle of HIV) – all by Grégoire Cirade.

Translated from French by Peter Lewis

PROJECT TEAM
Series editor Christine Noble
Art editor Julie Bennett
Designer Martin Bennett
Consultant Ruth Binney
Proofreader Ron Pankhurst
Indexer Marie Lorimer

Colour origination FMG
Printed and bound in China

VIVAT DIRECT
Editorial director Julian Browne
Art director Anne-Marie Bulat
Managing editor Nina Hathway
Picture resource manager Sarah Stewart-Richardson
Technical account manager Dean Russell
Product production manager Claudette Bramble
Production controller Sandra Fuller

We are committed both to the quality of our products and the service we provide to our
customers. We value your comments, so please feel free to contact us on 0871 3511000
or via our website at **www.readersdigest.co.uk**

If you have any comments or suggestions about the content of our books, you can
email us at **gbeditorial@readersdigest.co.uk**

CONCEPT CODE: FR0104/IC/S
BOOK CODE: 642-013 UP0000-1
ISBN: 978-0-276-44525-5